C A T A C L Y S M
When Human Stories Meet Earth's Faults

The 7.5 Hebgen Lake earthquake and rockslide,
near midnight of August 17, 1959,
killed 28 people.

Survivors recall their night of fear and
the meaning of being spared.

Earth scientists speaking then and now
examine this awesome earth-building event
as we consider the temporal span of human life in the planet's constant re-creation.

By Douglas W. Huigen

Skifoot Press
Spokane, Washington

Photographs by the author unless otherwise credited.

Aerial photographs by Doug Chapman, Montana Aircraft, Inc., Belgrade, Montana.

Cover illustration: U.S. Geological seismograph of 1959 Hebgen earthquake.
Graphics by David Sams.

Typesetting and page design by Cory Santiago and David Sams.

"Fire and Ice" from *The Poetry of Robert Frost"* edited by Edward Connery Lathem.
Copyright 1923, 1969 by Henry Holt and Company. Copyright 1951 by Robert Frost.
Reprinted by permission of Henry Holt and Company, LLC.

Publisher's Cataloging-in-Publication Data

Huigen, Douglas W.
CATACLYSM: When Human Stories Meet Earth's Faults / Douglas W. Huigen
Includes bibliographical references and glossary.

ISBN 978-0-9823623-0-3

1. Earthquakes. 2. Geology. 3. Personal narratives.

Printed in Shanghai, China by USA DiYa Corporation

Skifoot Press
P. O. Box 9715, Spokane, Washington 99209
(509) 328-3158

Contents

Introduction

Fifty years ago — just before midnight on Aug. 17, 1959 — a mountain poised on the edge of calamity finally split apart, thundered into the canyon below and instantly buried 19 campers where they slept. Rock rubble 230 feet deep obliterated Rock Creek Campground. The blast of air, water and trees blown aside by the slide tumbled and either killed outright or fatally injured others camped at the edges of the slide. Still others survived, or were spared, as some prefer to say. Of one family of six, only two survived.

The triggering Hebgen Lake Earthquake was the largest in the Rocky Mountains known in historic times and one of the largest earthquakes ever recorded in the United States, with a magnitude of 7.5 on the Richter scale. The slide was the second largest known in the nation.

Events that night significantly changed the landscape of southwestern Montana's Madison River Canyon. Most dramatic were the collapsed mountain and creation of a new lake at the western end of the cataclysm. Further upstream on the river, old fault lines deepened, opening new scars. A man-made lake and dam, both of which somehow survived, were part of a Denver-sized section of the earth's crust that sank, essentially in two adjacent blocks, by as much as 22 feet.

Temporal human life became a brief chaotic moment, a thin slice of time, in eons of Earth's perpetual change.

When people narrowly escape certain, sudden death by natural forces totally beyond their control, how do they behave? What do they think? Feel? Believe? Do they wonder why they were spared and others nearby were not? Is "spared" even the right word? How has the experience impacted their lives?

How do we make peace with the accident of being there precisely at the time earth movements millions of years in the making reach their tipping point and crumble mountains apart?

This book explores the interface between human choices/behavior/understanding and the neutral/anonymous forces of nature which simultaneously tear down and build up Earth.

Among the campers in the quake area that night, unknowingly staked out less than a quarter mile from a major fault line, were two geologists who had been in the field all summer conducting a survey to unlock the area's rocky secrets. *Voila'*. Some of those secrets fell into their laps, like manna from heaven. As with the human questions, the geologic issues are unending. Now, 50 years after the event, this geologically volatile region still poses questions and differing answers. Geologists, I've discovered, are good at that.

Fascination with the stories survivors might tell goaded me into this project. I hoped that retelling their experiences would also tell the story of the quake and slide, but soon my research pulled me deeper into the equally fascinating history and dynamics of these mountains and canyons, especially their faults — geologically speaking, of course.

How do the forces that created this awesome terrain now break it apart? These changes usually occur so gradually only extremely sensitive technology can quantify them. But once in a long, long while gradualism takes a back seat to the sudden release of energy such as represented in the Hebgen faulting, quake and rockslide.

It was earth-building in the truest sense, visible in our own lifetime.

The odds say it will be many lifetimes before something like this happens again.

Other threats, moving slower, involved water. Many survivors scrambled up the north slope of the canyon, forced to flee the rising Madison River. The damming effect of the slide had immediately started to create a new lake. A husband and wife, each near 70, spent the night climbing ever higher in a tree, clinging to one another and calling into the darkness for help as rising water inched up on them. More than one person, according to various reports, became pinned beneath timber knocked over by the air and water blast. Family members spent anxious efforts trying to free them while the water rose, sometimes as high as their chests, before the logs floated free and released them.

Just as the earthquake itself resulted from the sudden release of pent-up pressures in stressed rock strata, huddled refugees feared the potential failure of Hebgen Dam. It had been built in 1915 dangerously close to an ancient fault line which apparently, at the time, was not known to exist.

The quake collapsed old two-lane Montana Highway 287 into Hebgen Lake, blocking escape to the east. Tilting earth reconfigured Hebgen Lake's northern shoreline, moving it further north. Even today, you can see a disintegrating path of asphalt disappear into Hebgen Lake only to reappear on a shoreline across a bay one-half mile away. Correspondingly, the tilted lake's old south shoreline also moved north, further exposed.

All through the night, people heard rocks tumbling down near them as after-shocks shook the canyon.

For weeks government officials worried about the new lake filling up to the crest of the slide then cutting down through it. How dangerous was this threat to the town of Ennis, Montana, 44 miles away, and other habitation downstream on the Madison River?

Survival has many shades of meaning. A survivor can be purely passive; his or her body is suddenly traumatized and tossed around until coming to rest still breathing and eventually conscious, alive but through no discernable intention or escape strategy. Or, one awakens to a tremendous roar, panics through a tent flap or a camp-trailer window and starts scrambling, almost anywhere that seems to be away from the threatening sound. Or, you keep climbing higher in a tree. Or later, perhaps gathered into a huddle with others, you start contemplating possible dangers yet to materialize.

These are adrenaline-filled minutes and hours when our natural stress defense system prepares us for fight or flight. In that condition we react before we've had time to give the threat much rational thought. One woman told me, however, that the real survival skills came into play much, much later, after the initial trauma and grief for loss of family had passed.

These interviews included one persistent question: How has survival — being spared when persons close to you died — affected your life?

I suppose it is a question that one does not have to have been through an earthquake to ask. It's just that these folk did or still do ponder that question — or, in some cases, never have been troubled by it.

I regret being unable to trace families of persons buried in the slide. Finding even the survivors was difficult and sometimes serendipitous. I think often of the relatives and friends of those believed to have been lost in the slide. Some knew from news reports of the quake that their loved ones were probable victims. Others, not knowing vacation itineraries, just did not hear from their loved ones again — ever.

Would those stories cast this book in an entirely different perspective? The question is unanswerable.

At the time of the Hebgen earthquake, I was nearly 1,000 miles away in Iowa hoping to find a newspaper job in Montana. By phone, an editor told me he didn't have an opening that fit me. I remember how my disappointment was overshadowed by his excitement telling about the quake. He had felt the shaking nearly 300 miles away in the quiet of his darkroom while developing film and printing photographs, for which his newspaper was famous.

Less than two weeks after the quake, with my wife and baby daughter, we towed a U-Haul trailer to western Montana to start a new life. My parents, confirmed flat-landers, thought we were crazy for moving to such a "dangerous" place.

Hearing follow-up quake stories — and having second thoughts about a difficult new job for which I had come nearly halfway across the country — my curiosity became occupied by questions about the myriad decisions that leave us in harm's way or allow us opportunity to thrive. Add to this the human interface with nature's forces — some of which are arbitrary and unforeseen, some predictable.

Chapter 1 briefly tells what happened, to set context for the stories in Chapters 2-7 and 9 by people caught in the chaos. Chapter 8 captures reactions of tourists passing through who learn of the event for the first time. Chapters 10 and 11 deal with the geology — past, present and future.

I hope readers can empathize with and celebrate these survivors' journeys, and their calling our attention to a magnificent story of earth-building. Creative forces in the earth and our lives will endure, as will our interpretations of them.

You will find conflicting interpretation of geologic events reported here. That perhaps is expected in a science whose material is mostly unseen. Seeking confirmation of information and new perspectives on a story often invites confounding diversity and conflict. Several times I found myself resisting the idea of gaining even one more divergent opinion. As one of my geologist sources said of pursuing more data, "I wrote a book once and found that the last 10 percent took half the time, and that cured me."

I hope this book represents various viewpoints fairly without taking sides, encouraging inquiry into our certainties as well as our uncertainties. To you, the reader, welcome to the adventure of discovery.

— Doug Huigen, February 2009

Acknowledgements

One person stands out as I think of all who have helped make this book possible. Joanne Girvin, director of the Madison River Canyon Earthquake Area's Visitor Center, provided a wealth of information and encouragement from the very start. She helped me find survivors and guided me to information sources. Every time I contacted her she responded with new insights and a wonderfully cheerful attitude about the project's success. I am forever grateful to her.

Of course, there are the survivors who gave first-hand accounts of escaping that terrifying night: Irene Bennett Dunn, who died in April 2007, and her son Phil Bennett; Bonnie Schreiber; the Rev. Elmer and Ruth Ost, both of whom have died since interviews, and their four children Larry Ost, Jerre Boba, Joan Gregory, and Shirley Johnson; Mildred "Tootie" Greene; and John Owen. They all had vivid memories and stories to tell, and I appreciate their forthrightness — even as our conversations triggered painful reliving of the events.

I remember quite well the day Joanne off-handedly remarked that she thought one of the geologists camped in the area the night of the quake might still be living. I found Irving J. Witkind's phone number by some internet sleuthing. We conversed in August 2007. He spoke with deliberate accuracy as each memory seemed to spark more enjoyment of telling about events half a lifetime in the past. Wit, as his colleagues past and present called him, kept reassuring his wife — and me — that he was okay and wasn't tired. He died six months later, in February 2008, a month shy of his 91st birthday.

Wit opened several other research doors for me. For example, he told me how to find Jack B. Eptstein, his assistant that summer. They and Epstein's wife and kid brother were camped practically on top of the quake's epicenter. Jack and I spent several hours together dredging up recollections. He gave invaluable assistance on technical matters and leads to other sources. Jack kept saying, "This is fun. I haven't thought about this stuff for years." He now volunteers almost half-time to special U. S. Geological Survey projects out of the agency's Washington, D.C., headquarters. Many thanks, Jack.

Wit also prompted me to contact an old adversary of his, Warren Hamilton, who unbeknownst to me lived not far away in the same Denver area. The two had disagreed sharply about interpretation of the quake, yet Wit urged me to contact Hamilton, who kindly agreed to talk with me. Although he's also long retired, Hamilton's home office has maps and other technical data close at hand, plus an exhaustive, carefully catalogued collection of excellent photographs he'd made around the world.

I appreciate the help of currently active geologic scientists of the USGS and other organizations. They spoke with high regard for both Witkind and Hamilton, but also explained how earth studies had changed over time. Mary Beth Marks, geologist for the Gallatin National Forest, in which the earthquake occurred, provided background perspective. Since this quake is closely related to the whole geology of Yellowstone National Park, I contacted Henry "Hank" Heasler, park geologist, who gave valuable insights regarding the region's thermal activity. Librarian Jackie Jerla of the Yellowstone Association's research archives offered gracious assistance. Current USGS personnel include David P. Schwartz, Suzanne Hecker, J. Michael O'Neill, and Kathleen M. Haller; all provided fascinating, patient, and uncondescending explanations of these complex geologic processes to a rank non-geologist. Thanks also to Diane I. Doser, professor in the Department of Geological Sciences, University of Texas at El Paso, who was at the University of Utah when she first studied the Hebgen and Red Canyon faults. I've learned to admire the breadth of expertise and work pace of Robert B. Smith, professor of geology and geophysics at the University of Utah and supervisor of the Yellowstone Volcano Observatory (YVO), a research and hazard forecasting collaboration of the USGS, University of Utah and Yellowstone National Park. The YVO is set up to anticipate and warn government officials and the public of changes in the volcanic system underlying Yellowstone country.

Special thanks to all the people who have read various versions of the manuscript and offered comments and suggestions, including friends Stan Grant and Eileen Starr, both retired geology professors, Dale Avery, a geologist retired from the Bureau of Mines, Jack Epstein, who was mentioned above, and my wife Diane, for her editing and patience over the past three years. I greatly appreciate the work of David Sams and Cory Santiago in designing and composing text and illustration layouts, and to retired USGS staffer Avery J. Rendon for his adaptations of Epstein's USGS map of the West Yellowstone Basin, inside front cover.

Montana pilot-photographer Doug Chapman, dodging almost daily smoke haze, wonderfully captured the scenes I desired, plus others I had no way of anticipating. He flies out of Belgrade and West Yellowstone.

And perhaps most of all, I say "thank you" to all those friends who, over the past few months, were perhaps astonished to learn I was writing about geology, but did not throw cold water — or stones.

— Doug Huigen, January 2009

Chapter 1

Aug. 17, 1959: The Event

When the Hebgen Lake earthquake hit southwestern Montana, near midnight on Monday, Aug. 17, 1959, 26 people were killed outright. Of that toll, 19 persons were buried in a heart beat as a mountain split from the top, and the resulting rockslide (Fig. 5) barreled downward to overrun Rock Creek Campground, burying it under rock rubble at least 230 feet deep. Four members of a family of six died as they were blown away by the blast of air and river water suddenly displaced by the slide; the mother and a son survived. About six miles away, a husband and wife sleeping in their tent were crushed as a car-sized boulder bounded off a mountain and invaded their campsite at Cliff Lake, missing their three sons sleeping outside. The 27th and 28th known and final victims, among the first persons air-lifted out, died of their injuries at a Bozeman, Montana, hospital the day after the quake and slide. At least 150 campers survived the night with various degrees of trauma. Many believed they were trapped in the canyon, perhaps doomed. Rescue took several hours to come.

Geologists tell us a long horizontal buttress of dolomitic rock that supported the rocks above gave way in the earthquake, allowing the collapse of an estimated 37 million cubic yards of loose rock weighing 80 million tons. Today the mound spans a mile between its upstream and downstream edges and three-fourths of a mile from its leading edge on the north to the trailing rubble. Only one other landslide in U. S. history is known to be larger.

It's dizzying to contemplate this much material plummeting over campsites at nearly 100 miles an hour, as calculated later.

Blaming the failed dolomite buttress, however, is only part of the story. The downward-sloping layers of weathered gneiss and schist rock (Fig. 37), primed to slide, assumed an almost fluid quality as the quake's jolt changed gravity's claim on the rock mass, freeing its flow across the canyon.

Dolomite fractured with the quake's shaking and led the monstrous rush down the mountain's north-facing slope, floating to rest at the top edge of the slide 400 feet up the canyon's other side. Felled trees scattered on the slide surface, although uprooted, appeared to be distributed as they had been on the mountainside.

One of the most remarkable landmarks is a boulder the size of a small house (Fig. 1) at the leading edge of the slide. It had been part of the structure which gave way. This piece of the fractured buttress literally rode atop the plastic flow of loose rock. There were no indications that the boulder tumbled. Lichens still clinging to its side are clues to its having "floated" through the chaos, buoyed up on a cushion as the earthquake's vibrations fluidized the rock debris.

The boulder provides a commanding view of the slide rubble, the Earthquake Lake Visitor Center below, and the hollowed-out mountain across the way. Bolted to the boulder's face is a bronze plaque memorializing 28 victims — those 19 persons believed to have been buried below and nine others who died in related events (Fig. 56 and Appendix).

Not everyone had recognized the shaking as an earthquake, which was later found to measure 7.5 on the Richter scale and was one of the largest ever recorded in the United States. Not until dawn did Rock Creek campers, whose tents and camp trailers were bowled over at the very edge of the giant rock fall, realize how close they came to certain death just a few hours before. And all of the eventual evacuees feared drowning if Hebgen Dam failed and they hadn't yet reached higher ground.

Only after the dust settled the next day — literally, for a full moon lit the clouds of dust arising from numerous landslides and rock falls as after-shocks rattled all night throughout the area — did geologists discover the quake's cause. Two old fault lines, their scarps having become obscure in the thousands of years since their last fracture, had reactivated, the ground falling as much as 22 feet. A scarp is the visible, surface manifestation of a fault, or fracture, in bedrock far below. The scarp often is in loose, unconsolidated material such as soil or gravel. The Hebgen faults are normal faults, vertical drops with one side of the fracture falling relative to the high side. Strike-slip faults show a horizontal displacement, shearing left or right, such as the San Andreas fault along the Pacific coast. Faults in which the rocks on one side are pushed over those on the other side are called thrust or reverse faults.

Thinking of the subsidence of these Hebgen and Red Canyon fault scarps, however, focuses the mind on only a small portion of the land movement involved. Actually nearly all of the West Yellowstone Basin, approximately 150 square miles, dropped an average of 10 feet, as if hinged on its southern and eastern borders and tilting downward toward the northwest. Atop this falling block, which probably is several miles thick, sits Hebgen Lake, which like its surrounding terrain subsided virtually as a unit. The tilting block, however, lowered the northern shoreline

and exposed the southern, and in one location buried a section of highway hugging the northern shore.

Also subsiding a similar amount was the Red Canyon block, an area of 25 square miles adjacent to the Hebgen block and ranging up the mountainside to the northeast.

Fueling fears that the quake might have weakened Hebgen Dam was the additional threat caused by seiche (pronounced saysh) activity on the lake. A seiche is a slow, rolling shift of water from one end of a container to the other. The effect is similar to carrying a flat pan of water and bumping your elbow going through a door. The Hebgen quake caused this kind of sloshing. The first waves to hit the concrete-core earth-fill dam were estimated topping it by about 4 feet, causing some erosion of the downstream earth fill. The dam sustained cracks, some as wide as 6 inches, but still stands today. Destruction of summer cabins on the north shore also resulted from the seiche activity and the triple-pronged effect of: 1) block subsidence, 2) flooding of the lowered shoreline and 3) slumping of newly water-logged soil into the lake. One woman awakened by the commotion reported jumping off her cabin porch to the trembling, slumping earth just as the cabin collapsed into the lake behind her.

Survivors straggled through the night to a high point in the canyon they dubbed Refuge Point. It offered a refuge barely higher than the lake level should the dam fail. After-shocks kept everyone on edge. The high ground also had enough flat area to allow helicopters to land the next day. With the injured going first, most of the survivors were ferried out before the end of the day.

Massive rescue efforts soon overwhelmed Gallatin and Madison County law enforcement agencies. Volunteers joined U. S. Forest Service, National Park Service, and Fish and Game

Department personnel. Also key were the helicopters, planes and Air Force personnel from Malmstrom Air Force Base at Great Falls, nearly 200 miles north. Survivors were critical, however, of some of the first pilots flying over the area at dawn apparently interested only in sight-seeing. Even if they had been inclined to land, however, there was little or no suitable landing area for fixed-wing aircraft as most of the nearby highway was buckled or cracked open by the quake (Fig. 41).

Damage to buildings was estimated at $1.7 million in 1959 dollars, with an additional $2.6 million for highway repair. Highway 287 and part of Highway 191 had to be rebuilt.

The most urgent construction work was atop the huge slide near the west end of the Madison River Canyon. With newly formed Earthquake Lake rising an average of 9 feet per day, engineers feared that the inevitable topping of the slide dam could result in sudden erosion causing a catastrophic flood in the Madison Valley, especially in the town of Ennis, approximately 44 miles downstream. Earth movers and bulldozers worked around the clock to prepare a wide spillway that would withstand the Madison River's flow.

The lake's highest level backed water nearly up to the base of Hebgen Dam and obliterated Halford's Resort, about three miles below the dam. High water also flooded part of Campfire Resort, located on the Madison River about a mile below the dam. Engineers finally dropped the spillway level by 50 feet, lining the drain with the hard dolomite rock which once held up a mountainside. This drop uncovered the flooded Campfire Resort and created about two miles of free-flowing river between the dam and the head of Earthquake Lake. Halford's was never rebuilt.

With this overview of the event as background, now re-live these eye-witness accounts by survivors.

4

Chapter 2

SCHREIBER: They Usually Camped Elsewhere

"Of all places for a mountain to fall down," reminisces Bonnie Schreiber, who now lives on a ranch near Martinsdale, Montana, and was 7 years old the year of the quake. "Why did it pick that campground?"

Bonnie (Fig. 7) and her family had camped at Rock Creek Campground for years. This particular year they found their usual camp site "under a very large tree" already occupied, so they found another location about 100 yards away, closer to the eastern, upstream edge of the campground.

While the rockslide did not cover their campsite, the sudden burst of air, Madison River water, and trees violently displaced by the slide tumbled and thrashed their camp trailers and vehicles.

"The slide came down and hit the river, which hit our trailer and shoved it out of the way," Bonnie recalls, although for the most part her story is what she remembers hearing retold by her parents. Her father died a few years back. Her mother suffers from dementia, but her memory still flashes in and out of that night.

Although Bonnie's father quickly realized he faced something far more ferocious when he first heard the rumbling, Schreiber prepared himself to deal with a bear which had visited their campsite the night before and robbed their food cache of a ham.

"Dad grabbed a flashlight and hammer to hit the bear over the head," Bonnie relates. "He stepped outside and the trailer was about three feet in the air. He turned around and could not get back in. Mom looked out the window and saw a cloud of dust coming down the mountain.

"He reached for me but something hit our trailer and blew it aside.

"Mom and Dad said they heard the outfits hit together. Esther and Warren Steele were in a tent nearby. Grandma and Aunt Verona were in a Coleman pop-up tent trailer a little farther on. The water shoved us into Warren and Esther's car and then everything into Grandma and Verona's rig.

"Mom seen dad and called to him. He would rush over and walk away, over and over. Mom handed me out through the window and then crawled out herself. She took me up to where some other people were and put me in the back of a station wagon."

One of the things Bonnie remembers is being forced to drink a mixture of whiskey and milk, chosen perhaps for its availability more than its supposed therapeutic effects. She remembers towels wrapped around her head, because of a blow from the side near her right eye. There were early fears Bonnie might lose her eye, but her vision turned out fine.

"I looked out of that station wagon window and saw terror in my mother's face. I never saw it before nor since. It was dark, but people had flashlights and there were car headlights.

"Mom went back to find her other people.

"Esther started talking to this lady in the dark — 'Is this you, Mrs. Holmes?' 'Yes.' — and both sat there in prayer.

"My heart got beating fast here, just telling about it," and she paused for a moment.

The "lady in the dark" was Bonnie's aunt, Verona Holmes, who died in the autumn of 2004 after suffering much of her life with the ankle she injured that night when a log pinned her down.

Having survived the slide, rising water from the Madison River, dammed by displaced mountain rubble, created a new hazard for Verona.

"They had to wait for the water to rise and lift that tree to pull her out from under," Bonnie remembers.

Years later, with the repetitious daily treatment of her damaged ankle, Verona must have marveled how critically close we relate to water — an essential but sometimes pesky body fluid, a soothing balm, an attraction for our recreational pursuits, a personal threat of drowning as the water rose around her, and a blessing as it finally floated the log off her.

"Mom came back and said she had grandma," Bonnie continues, catching her breath. "Most of her clothes were torn off. Grandma said to 'leave me — take the others and leave.' She said she couldn't make it any more.

"Then two fellas came along and asked for the injured. They took care of grandma."

Then came the aftershocks.

"You could feel the ground shake and then hear boulders coming down the hill and then bounce over you. They piled a couple of suitcases over me to protect me from rocks. I could hear people shouting down in the bottom, clinging to trees."

About six miles up the Madison canyon was Hebgen Dam. With the earth still shaking, there was fear of the dam's collapse causing still further catastrophe. The Schreiber party and others had to reach higher ground.

High and dry up on a point elevated above the level of Hebgen Dam and Lake, survivors huddled together through the night, awaiting rescue. They would later learn the road along the north shore of Hebgen Lake was destroyed, having dropped as much as 22 feet, sinking nearly a half mile of roadway under the lake.

Bonnie remembers a nurse, Mildred "Tootie" Greene of Billings, helping comfort people. "She was one of the heroes, along with a Mr. Martin of Virginia City and Polly Weston.

"From the chopper, a doctor came and was impressed with what Tootie had done. He made a list of who was to go out first. Me, Grandma, Verona, Esther and Dad — it seems like we rode in a chopper to West Yellowstone, then in an airplane to Bozeman.

"In the ambulance, I heard someone say 'Hit it, she's starting to vomit.' When they put the stitches in, they had to do it without deadening the area because they had no idea whether I was allergic. Apparently they thought I was going to lose my right eye. But my right eye's fine." Bonnie still remembers Polly Weston holding her hand during the procedure.

While Verona and Esther were being ferried the 90 miles north to Bozeman, their small plane had a door fall open on take-off. The wind almost sucked out the nurse and Esther, but Esther held on and grabbed the nurse, according to Bonnie.

"They almost lost their lives in the air."

Why was this a favorite family place?

"My grandma, she was quite a fisherman. So what we did, we'd haul our boat on over to Wade Lake. We left the boat there and would drive over to fish … That was the only thing we saved out of the earthquake, was that boat and the boat motor."

She describes her father and a friend, Sigard Eagan of Absarokee, later going to retrieve the boat and finding about a hundred yards of the primitive road literally shaken apart — a set of wheel tracks fairly intact but each no more than two feet wide and with earth dropped down four or five feet in the middle and on both sides.

Her father balked but Sigard drove alone over the "elevated" tracks with his cattle truck, going to the boat and then bringing it back.

"'Aw, that's nothing,'" she quotes her father's friend. "That's Sigard. He could have lost everything right there."

And how does Bonnie look back now on having been on the edge of catastrophe?

"Well, I just (she takes a long pause) think there had to be a reason why God would do something for — yuh know, like that for us. We were lucky. We were able to get everybody on out, of our group. And uh, I don't know, it's just uh, it's just one of them things why the people that were parked by that tree were parked there, I don't know.

"But it just (Bonnie paused to clear her throat, her voice becoming more hesitant) turned out pretty good for us, to where we were able to get on out and not be buried under there someplace."

Even years after the event, standing on the slide rubble and viewing the scarred mountain that produced it, the sight gives a spiritual sensation of being present at the formation — and reformation — of the earth.

"It's spooky I'll tell ya," Bonnie says of a recent visit there. "The last time I was there, to pick up those tapes (of survivors' accounts of the experience) the wind was really really blowin' up there. I mean it was just a howlin'. Mom couldn't even open up the pickup door on her side, it was blowin' so hard, so I had to drive around to let her out and then I drove around so I could get out.

"But we got on in there (the visitors' center) and it was givin' kind of a woo woo, ya know, the wind was, and they were playin' that tape.

"And then I seen that picture of my grandma being loaded on the helicopter and that just startled me and I started cryin' and after that I started shakin', I was having trouble catching my breath and I just — it brought back a lot of memories. Cause I really loved my grandma. She was an OK person. . .

"To this day, my Mom and I, we're both a little bit leery of camping around mountains. You know, if there's a campground there, with an open space and there's a big mountain behind it we're kind of looking at it and thinking, well, we can just drive down the road a little ways further."

Bonnie laughs at herself easily, yet can turn serious in a flash and admit that sometimes just the rumble of a large truck wheeling past her home makes her think "earthquake."

Chapter 3

OWEN: Which Way to Safety?

Some people thought it was Armageddon.

Although skies over the Madison River Canyon were clear, there had been distant lightning and rolling thunder much of the night, reminding campers of nature's power from above.

Then, out of the blue, ending their sleep for the night, came the first huge jolts of the earthquake. Power from below.

John Owen, now an accountant living in Colorado (Fig. 8), was 15 at the time. His parents annually rented a cabin at Halford's Resort, which is located about 2 miles downstream from Hebgen Dam and about 4 miles upstream from Rock Creek Campground and the slide. They came for the fishing which makes Madison country famous.

As Californians, he tells me, they were used to hearing earthquakes build gradually, sounding like an approaching train. "But this was different, much more sudden."

The initial quake was not "a shake and stop. It lasted maybe 30 to 45 seconds, but probably no more than a minute.

"The quake was followed by the thunder of it," John says of the slide, although no one in his group knew until later what had caused the roar.

What they heard, but could not see until morning, was one of the largest landslides ever recorded. This massive chunk of the earth's crust did not come down in dribbles and dabs, but

as a unit. No wonder people hearing it from afar had visions of Armageddon.

John recalls, "It seemed to last quite a while. I imagine it (the slide) had to take a minute or two to come all the way down the mountain and stop. It was a horrific noise."

Excited, anxious talk prevailed as the Owen family joined vacationers from other cabins, milling about in the moonlight, trading puzzled conjectures.

The big jolt hit Montana during the Cold War, which lasted from the mid-1940s until the early 1990s. The Korean War was over. But the imminent installation of 150 Minuteman Intercontinental Missiles around Malmstrom Air Force Base at Great Falls, 270 miles to the north, possibly placed Montana on the front lines of a next big war. It would not be long until the Berlin Wall (1961-89), the Cuban Missile Crisis (1962), and the Vietnam War (1964-75).

"A confrontation with Russia was on people's minds," John remembers. "I know there were some people who reacted that way, that maybe this was a bomb, like THE BIG EVENT.

"Fortunately, it was just an earthquake." He laughs.

Halford's owner, Hank Powers, a teacher and coach who operated the resort only during the three summer months, had an evacuation plan, unused, due to the perceived threat posed by old Hebgen Dam and the 386,000 acre feet of water behind it. He rounded up his guests, urging them to evacuate quickly to avoid the potential flood.

Halford's sat on the river at the foot of a huge hill of glacier- and water-borne sand and gravel measuring approximately two miles wide and topping out some 300 feet above the river level. Beaver Creek, flowing into the Madison from the north, splits the delta, or fan. Geologists believe the mound is made up of rubble scoured out of the Beaver Creek drainage — carried by water over the ages or by ice during one or more of the three known glacial periods that sculpted the area, the oldest known some two million years ago and the latest as recent as 14,000 years ago.

A primitive road immediately beside the river led away from the resort, allowing one to drive upstream, toward the dam, or downstream, toward the slide which they would learn about later. Most chose the latter, but took a gamble as they gunned their vehicles over the sizeable gaps where earthen approaches of the roadway had separated from both ends of the Beaver Creek bridge.

Those who chose upstream were on a dirt road that climbed up and away from the river's edge only about 200 feet away from the base of the 87-foot-high dam structure. They drove through water — remember it was near midnight and dark — as water sloshed over the top of the dam. The quake had caused large seiche waves to surge back and forth across the lake until almost noon the next day.

"Water got up to their hubcaps but they continued on," John says. "They were okay, other than being scared to death."

Where the resort access road joined Montana Highway 287, John's family and their neighbors met other quake evacuees for the first time and only then learned of the slide. This was the

"big event," only different from what they had pictured in their minds.

People came from the west, for the westward exit from the canyon was blocked by the slide. People coming from the east found their way back toward West Yellowstone blocked by some 20 feet of water as the newly-tilted Hebgen Lake advanced its shoreline to the north, flooding the roadway.

Hank Powers directed everyone to the highest point on Highway 287 between Hebgen and the slide, now called Refuge Point. It was the same high ground sought by the Rock Creek campers.

Ironically, these campsite refugees from a variety of catastrophic natural forces found refuge atop a geologic structure built by ancient natural forces — gravity and its pull on running water and the glaciers.

It was here dozens of survivors spent the night, hearing the rush of the river far below, over the brow of the slope. They also heard falling rock rubble from above, loosened by aftershocks throughout the night. Puffs of dust rose into the moonlight, kicked up by rock falls.

I ask John if he had sensed people as hysterical.

"I saw fear," he says. "The aftershocks were a threat. People realized it was a quake. They knew they had to be on high ground if the dam broke.

"But for the most part people were very helpful to one another, consoling each other, trying to keep calm."

And how has this experience shaped John's life?

"Without a doubt, this event stands out in my memory.

"It was sad, obviously. I wouldn't say traumatic.

"But it was certainly a point in my life I'll never ever forget. Other than my two tours in Vietnam, it's got to be my number two thing that I will remember the most.

"And I keep going back to it, showing people what an amazing thing it was and how, for whatever reason, that slide came down the mountain, and I decided that was the end of that."

John's quake clippings filled a scrapbook as part of his science project the next school year.

"I've always been interested in science and geology. I go back often … I went back the year after and every year that I could. I take my kids up there."

John now owns 20 acres about five miles downstream from the slide, just beyond the western-most ridge of the Madison Range. There the river, which has rapidly flowed mostly westerly out of Yellowstone National Park, turns northward and meanders through the broad Madison Valley, toward Ennis, a trout-fishing paradise. Further north it tumbles roughshod through yet another canyon before peacefully joining the Gallatin and Jefferson rivers to form the Missouri River at Three Forks, Montana.

The quake was the climax of an era for John.

"It ended my family vacation time with my mom and dad on a high note." He laughs. "You could call it a low note or a high note.

"It was the fifties. When I was that age fishing was great, mom and dad were great and everything about it made me think very positive, and there's an end to that era.

"Today, it couldn't be the same as it was then even though it might be the same place. You know, time changes things, and me, too."

Had he ever wondered if a big slide might have come down across the river at Halford's Resort? A small one did.

Yes, it had crossed their minds, but that part of the canyon was less steep, and wider.

"And. . ." John pauses, uttering a guttural "huh," then pausing again before another "huh," and continuing:

"So I'll throw this out.

"The day before, we were going to fish at Rock Creek (site of the slide). Hank, my dad and myself. We were going to go down there and fish because the river had a big, big corner, a steep wall on the far side, and a big old deep hole.

"We went through the campground and thought there were too many people so we went on. Ironic," says John, who insists he's not superstitious.

On that line of thought, hearing there were people who had planned to camp there that night but went on, John's reply was that some of the people buried by the slide probably stayed there by accident, not by plan. A reverse fate equally hard to explain.

Asked about destiny versus accidental consequences, John sees no purpose or causality involved.

"It was a day in history and we happened to be nearby. I ended up later being in Vietnam and obviously recall a lot of that. And my attitude at this point is kind of the same. I was fortunate that I went through it fairly unscathed.

"And I look back at that, too, as I had a chance to be involved in something and it didn't hurt me too awfully bad. And while others, an awful lot of others, suffered greatly, it hasn't changed, nor the earthquake hasn't changed. . .

"I don't think. . .

"I'm sure. . .

"Yeah. . ."

Then, resigned to uncertainty, John continues: "Who knows if it's changed your life. You have a lot of decisions to make, and who knows?

"I know I haven't avoided rivers. I haven't avoided cliffs. I haven't stopped fishing."

Had his parents talked of it?

"Yeah, but not a whole lot."

But he quickly moves the subject to the next day when he and his father twice returned to their cabin down at river level to gather and retrieve their fishing tackle.. "My job was to stay outside and feel for aftershocks and listen for anything that sounded like Hebgen Dam breaking.

"In that case, if the dam let loose, we were going to run like heck up the hill."

John also remembers taking the time to set free the chipmunks he had live-trapped whenever he wasn't fishing. The quake's horrors do not dull his sense of humor in the tangential events.

While they gathered fishing gear and set chipmunks free, the Madison River flowing past them was becoming a lake, advancing slowly back toward Halford's Resort. By 6:30 o'clock that morning, water was 20 feet deep at the slide. Three weeks later the new Earthquake Lake was about 200 feet deep and flooded the canyon above nearly to the base of Hebgen Dam.

What happened to Halford's Resort?

Log cabins at the resort literally floated off their foundations and prevailing westerly winds drifted them upstream with the rising waters. In October, when engineers feared for the safety of people and property downstream, they dropped the new lake's level by excavating the spillway 50 feet deeper. They strengthened the channel against erosion by bulldozing in a lining of the dolomite that had once buttressed the mountain.

As Earthquake Lake's level dropped, the Halford cabins settled down wherever they had drifted. One small collection of cabins is called "Ghost Village." John says his family's usual cabin has fallen apart, but others he still recognizes. It's hard to imagine any log tourist cabin surviving all this.

John and his family and friends often fish this short stretch of the Madison River, between Hebgen Dam and Earthquake Lake. The road which used to serve the resort now is blocked off, canyon access limited to a peaceful hiking trail. Its serenity as you walk it in golden late-afternoon sun, insects emerging and skimming the river, masks the terror which once haunted the place.

An RV and tent camp and restaurant thrive not far upstream, even closer to the still-standing Hebgen Dam. And across the highway, at Cabin Creek Campground, families pitch their tents a few dozen feet from the western end of the Hebgen fault scarp.

Halford's Resort owner Hank Powers and his wife, both teachers in Twin Falls, Idaho, are no longer living. Nor are John's parents.

"The owners and my mom and dad knew each other for many years. We camped there every August. My dad died about seven years after the quake. Mrs. Powers died about a year later.

"And the next thing I know, Mr. Powers is down in California knocking on my mom's door, and saying 'hello.' She was over 50. He was over 60. And so they got married."

John was away in school. He became an accountant and in recent years has specialized in consulting with companies whose growth has outpaced their management skills, and thus they must change tactics to regain stability.

His work sounds a bit like life skills he might have learned as a teen-ager, riding out an earthquake's shaky ground.

Chapter 4

GREENE: Studied First-Aid Just in Time

"I only did what I could," says Mildred "Tootie" Greene of those first few hours after the quake.

Tootie, her husband Ramon, and young son Steve (Fig. 9) were among the campers who set up just beyond the slide's reach. Fortunately, they were not further west, where they usually camped. Because of the crowd, they were camped on a ridge above the main campground. Still, water, mud, and falling timber forced out by the slide collapsed one end of their large, 18-foot tent. Luckily, they were sleeping at the other end but even so were nearly trapped inside. It was not until the next day they became aware their clothing was muddy up to their waists.

Tootie remembers the ground rolling like "ocean waves" and "noise you couldn't believe," then "a wall of water coming right straight at us," clouds of dust later discovered to be from the slide, and campers stumbling through the chaos, many naked, their nightclothes ripped off.

The Greenes' car started but could not go anywhere. Ray gunned the engine but the rear drive wheels spun freely. He then discovered that the blast of air and water had pushed a large uprooted tree under the car, high-centering it, and wedged two trees into the far side of the car.

"It's now buried under water. The insurance company bought that," Tootie laughs with me, seated with clippings and other quake memorabilia spread across her kitchen table in Billings. "And the canned cherries must still be down there, too. We won't live long enough to know if they find them or not."

Perhaps it is her ability to see the light as well as the dark side of a situation that made her a valued helper during rescue. With Ray's car engine running and headlights shining, it didn't take long for other survivors to be attracted their way.

Tootie the survivor suddenly became Tootie the nurse.

Only a month before vacation she had taken a Red Cross first aid class. As a 30-year-old nurse she knew how to function in a hospital with all kinds of equipment close at hand, but she said she realized how little she knew about surviving out in the woods. A Boy Scout across the street from the Greenes was taking a Red Cross class, so his mother and Tootie signed up, too. After the standard class, they also took an advanced class.

"The only ones I remember taking care of were the Painters," Tootie says. "The Painter girl came running up and said, 'Don't leave. My mother lost her arm.'" Tootie found the arm still attached but the woman was losing blood fast. Tootie's heavy bandaging stemmed the flow, although Mrs. Painter died several days later in the Bozeman hospital. Mr. Painter had a gash in his thigh deep enough to see bone.

It was chaos.

Although she had to be reminded of it later, a man from British Columbia, camped in an area closest to the slide, came to her for help. One ear had been completely torn from his head. His wife had tree twigs driven into her knee joints, a phenomenon sometimes reported from tornadoes.

She remembers Margaret "Grandma" Holmes, although seriously injured, walking away from the camp and up the mountainside only to die of her injuries the next day after helicopter evacuation to a Bozeman hospital.

Her daughter, Verona Holmes, had a badly damaged ankle, so severe the doctors urged amputation, but she refused. It crippled her for the remainder of her life.

"The Scotts from California … He almost lost a thumb and had internal injuries," Tootie recalls. "His wife knew she wasn't up to par but there was nothing visible that I could tell. We found out later she had a ruptured bladder.

"A couple of men had minor visible injuries, cuts and scratches, but they were in the most shock and shock is hard to treat." Why were men in greater shock?

"Maybe you don't want to hear this but men aren't all that manly in many situations," she says with a chuckle. "Many years later I realized how much it had affected my husband." In an interview after the quake, Ray recalled the slide's "awful noise, I will never forget. It was like an old steam engine going a hundred or two hundred miles an hour at full throttle. And in seconds it was over with."

She remembers the Grover Maults, in their 70s at the time, escaping rising water first on the roof of their camp trailer then climbing into a nearby tree, inching up limb by limb the rest of the night. Mrs. Mault clung to her husband's legs and feet but urged him to let her go and save himself. It was near dawn before Montana Power Co. released a boat to make a rescue possible. Years later, touring the slide and Earthquake Lake area, the elderly Mr. Mault was so emotionally shaken from the visit he could not walk.

Tootie recalls a man who had served as a dentist during World War II telling her he'd not seen war injuries as serious as those suffered by this group on Refuge Point.

Tootie obtained codeine, demerol, and aspirin from the dentist. She scrounged any useable supplies she could from fellow campers: "They bring everything but the kitchen sink and some of them had that, too." Waiting for an airlift out, they spelled out SOS on the highway with pancake mix.

She was busy until 3 o'clock the next day, when most of the injured had been evacuated.

What was their emotional state? Tootie said she did not hear people talking about doom. They weren't screaming. "There were a lot of people helping. We gathered the injured ones close together in vehicles."

And her emotional state? What difference has the experience made in her life? Has it changed her life pattern?

"Not too much," she says. "I trained to be a nurse. Helping comes naturally. There are many instances of people needing to stay in our home, either overnight or an extended stay.

"I really do think I was intended to be there. I don't think we plan our lives. Our lives are planned for us." No accidents? I ask. "No accidents," she says with a laugh.

"Like my brother said after a frightening plane ride — 'I could have been killed. But if it's your time, it's your time.'

"But what if it had been the pilot's time?" she'd asked him, then answered her own question: "Then it would have been yours, too."

Tootie definitely feels her family was "spared." On the closing page of an article she wrote but never published, she says, "Most people don't realize what their friends and relatives think of them until it's too late for them to appreciate it. We're among the fortunate few who escaped death so closely and to be shown so much love and concern."

She moved conversation on to a study group held at her church a few years back. Participants were reading the book *On Death and Dying,* by Elisabeth Kübler-Ross: "People did not want to talk about dying," she says, puzzled by their reluctance, a well as her own readiness, to discuss death.

She recalled a physician at her hospital once apologizing to a family because there was nothing more he could do. She says, "There comes a time when there's no more to do — no cure, no miracle." She says the same about husband Ray's death of cancer — "He would not have wanted to prolong the suffering."

Immediately she flashes back to that night in the Madison River canyon, survivors huddled at Refuge Point, the rush of the river below audible and the old dam upstream from them still perceived as a threat. "The sound of thunder was a blessing. It diverted people. I think I did more just being there, trying to keep things up instead of down."

Son Steve, who was 9 years old at the time, never has paid much attention to his mother's collection of clippings and memories. "All he could remember," Tootie says, "was the helicopters and how big a deal that was."

After he reached adulthood, Steve went back, although he told his mother nothing of his trip until years later. He saw the tilted lake, the cracked dam, the ominous slide, the historic displays at the visitors' center.

"Mom, you did good," he told her. She treasures that.

Chapter 5

"Rumbling Followed by a Terribly Ripping Sound"

Back home in Queens, New York, on hot nights with bedroom windows open and the "L" (elevated commuter train) making its distant racket, the Ost family remembered a night in Montana when they were only a few campsites away from sudden death.

First, the slide produced "a rumbling followed by a terribly ripping sound," says one daughter. Sounds of almost any train bring back the experience of her family's escape, frightened but nearly unscathed from the Hebgen earthquake and slide in Madison Canyon.

The adult children of the Rev. Elmer and Ruth Ost, both deceased, are: Larry Ost, then 14 and now head of a Chicago company that makes large industrial air filters; Jerre Boba, then 13, now a high school mathematics teacher living in Gilbert, AZ; Joan Gregory, then 11, now a transcription quality assurance worker for a national company, living in Benton City, WA; and Shirley Johnson, then 6, who now with her husband operates a riding stable and school near Portland, OR. (See Fig. 10.)

The four decided to gather in California in the summer of 2006, as one of them said, "before the funeral." And they did. The family of six assembled for the first time in more than 40 years. Their weakening father, Elmer, died six weeks later. Their mother, Ruth, died in May 29, 2008, less than a year after her husband and eight months after being interviewed for this story.

The siblings speak of their reunion decision — gathering together at an opportune time — with the same wonder expressed as they note their first choice of campsites was one that would have been buried. They chose another location, Joan says, because "Dad said no, we should get into a regular camp spot and pay our fee. That would be something my dad would do — do it right."

Larry, who had the closest call, shrugs off the near tragedy as just part of a great western adventure. They had visited Glacier National Park and now were headed toward Yellowstone. "That whole trip was just a dynamite experience," he says, not intending a pun.

Larry was the last of four, preceded by his parents and sister Jerre, to emerge from their tent at the quake's first rumblings. He has a clear memory of "a muddy wall of water, about four feet high" — the surge of river water thrust aside by the slide — racing toward him. "I quickly ducked my head back inside and curled up in my sleeping bag."

The surge tumbled Larry and the tent some distance before he could tear himself free from inside, by hooking the tent fabric on a tree snag he'd been rolled up against.

Larry remembers summer nights back in Queens being awakened by what he dreamily thinks is a tidal wave, but quickly realizes is the sound of a train, about a mile away. "It reminded me of those sounds in the tent."

The water surge did not persist, making one gush up out of the riverbed, then receding, leaving mud and debris.

Elmer had barked for everyone to hold onto a tree — Jerre did — and he later remarked, according to mother Ruth, "That's the first time she's ever obeyed me."

Joan and Shirley were sleeping in the family's 1950 Buick. Both remember the two-ton car bouncing up and down, finally landing on some logs, perhaps swept there by the water surge. The interior temporarily stayed dry.

Joan fled the vehicle — she wanted to find a tree and avoid trouble with her father — just in time to get wet from the surge.

Shirley remembers first awakening with a vivid dream: The car was bouncing. Her sister Jerre had been learning to drive. "I was mad that she was driving because we were falling off a cliff and the car was tumbling down when I woke up."

And then: "Mother came into the car, (futilely) pressing on the brake because the car was dancing toward the trees. She got all banged up from the steering wheel, then got out and carried me to higher, dry ground." There, says Jerre, "Dad got us all together and accounted for."

The Ost family (rhymes with "cost," it's Swedish), like other refugees from Rock Creek Campground, spent the dark but full-moon night feeling fortunate but unsure what exactly had happened. It was too dark to see the slide near them although they were aware that water, for some reason, was pooling up below. They could see the outline of the far ridgeline, backlit by the moon. They felt aftershocks and heard rock falls all though the night. They huddled wet and chilly with the others.

"Dad tried to calm people down," Shirley says. "We lit a fire. Dad being a minister, I know that we prayed."

As dawn broke they were awed by the sight of new-born Earthquake Lake in which their cars and other belongings were submerged, by the gaping scar on the mountainside from which millions of tons of rock had split away, and by the huge mound of the slide — especially noting how close it was to where they had been sleeping.

Early in the morning, a helicopter flew over and dropped an envelope, the contents of which caused more alarm. The note said, "Fire on river bridge top, get going. Ost."

"When Elmer read that he wondered who knew he was there, never thinking that 'Ost' was the signature of the person writing it," Ruth told me. "At any rate, we now had the threat of an unknown forest fire adding to our fears."

Five days later, they made a recovery stop in Sheridan, WY, and visited Elmer's cousin, Orlo Johnson, formerly with the Forest Service. Orlo knew an Otto Ost who was a smoke jumper out of Missoula. Correspondence later confirmed that Otto indeed had worked as a smoke jumper the year before, but he did not know how the note could have been left in the envelope because the agency's fire messages were closely monitored.

Many years later the Osts visited daughter Shirley and family in Portland and by chance read in the newspaper that an Otto Ost had died and had been living in Gresham, OR, with his daughter. Ruth and Elmer also had lived in Gresham after Elmer's retirement, not knowing that the man whose misplaced message had dropped into their hands in Montana was living nearby in Oregon — with Queens, NY, and Chicago in between.

The trip west was a unifying experience, one intensified by the earthquake and slide. Their trip home to Queens — flown there by the Red Cross — was largely a time for reflection, not upon the things they lost, but the fact they all had survived.

Several still are spooked by train sounds, or even the once-soothing sound of running water.

"My dad would take us out to church camps," says Joan. "Once in Utah we were in a place similar to Madison Canyon, with river and mountains. We wanted to move on, but dad insisted we stay.

"Dad had to tell us stories all night long. We were scared it would happen again. Sounds of water scared us, and it's still there deep inside. Finally, we fell asleep with dad's stories."

Ruth remembered the panic she felt inside the Buick, when it finally stopped bouncing and moving uncontrollably, with the thought, "The rest of the family could not have lived through all this." Over the years, Ruth said, her dominant feeling was "just of God leading us, that's all."

Larry did not go with the family for the slide-show presentations his father did for church groups and other occasions. According to his mother, Larry also did not take much of a part in family conversation about their ordeal. "To him it was 'no big deal,'" Ruth said. "Well, that's him."

Shirley does not remember her father describing the experience predominantly in a religious sense: "He wasn't that kind of guy, although he was a Godly man, praying and reading his Bible every day. But he loved science and enjoyed the geology of it. But it was a human interest story, too, and that was part of why it was so fascinating to him.

"He would have a conviction on his own that God had his hand on our family," she says.

Jerre — who looks back at herself at the time as "a self-centered 13-year-old, self-absorbed adolescent totally concerned about me" — made her first return to the site in her 20s and realized for the first time "how awful it might have been."

What about attributing their survival to God? "I didn't," Jerre says. "We were just really lucky. To say, 'Oh, God saved us!' How can you say that? What about those people that didn't have a chance? They were asleep and that was it."

Jerre notes that she and other family members sometimes remember things differently, not always consistent, having varying perceptions. But there is one thing upon which they strongly agree.

"We just lost things, we didn't lose one another," Jerre says.

The siblings gathered again, for their mother's memorial service, on Aug. 16, 2008, in Chicago where Elmer and Ruth lived for 22 years.

When they had gathered two years earlier, before Elmer's death, Ruth reminded her children of their old habit of family devotions — "when they could corral us together," adds Shirley. Their theme throughout that 1959 trip had been Psalm 46. Shirley remembers her mother asking them to take a Bible and check the Psalm, saying, "It is interesting to read again."

The passage reads, ironically, in part:

"God is our refuge and strength,
an ever-present help in trouble.

Therefore we will not fear, though the earth give way
and the mountains fall into the heart of the sea, though
its waters roar and foam and the mountains quake
with their surging ..."

Fascinating to contemplate is this interface between that which we choose and that over which we have no control, and the story's importance to us.

Chapter 6

BENNETT: A Family Blown Away

"It was such a beautiful moonlit night that we didn't even put our tent up," Irene recalls. "We spread it on the ground, put our sleeping bags on it and wanted to enjoy the beauty of the moon. It was just a gorgeous night."

The Bennett family — mother Irene, father Purley or "Pud," children Carole, 17, Phil, 16, Tom, 10, and Susan, 5 — had started their vacation trip to Yellowstone National Park from their home in Coeur d'Alene, Idaho, two days earlier. They approached the park from the west, having come south, up the broad Madison River Valley, through Ennis, Montana, then eastward as the river flows through a fairly narrow canyon, the location of a U. S. Forest Service campground named Rock Creek. See Figs. 11 and 12.

But the Bennetts did not camp in the established campground. Although the campsites probably were all full — others had found it so — Irene remembers only that they chose a spot along the river before reaching the campground, half a mile on upstream. All that evening they saw only one couple, who went down to the river to fetch water.

"My husband and I woke — I don't know if the children did or not — but I remember my husband standing up. The earth was shaking. He reached ahold of a tree and that's all I know," Irene said.

Several published accounts at the time quoted Irene as saying she last saw her husband gripping a tree while the wind blast held him out perpendicular to the trunk, like a flag, before he was blown away. But she told me, nearly 50 years later, it was not true, that she had been misquoted.

"I just remember being in water.

"When I found myself the next morning I was pinned under a tree to where I couldn't get out. But I did cover myself — 'cause I was naked — with just branches and lay there for a while, then finally I decided to dig out. And I dug and dug in the river bed to get myself out from under the tree."

Mid-August's first light in western Montana comes at about 5 o'clock, or about five and a half hours after the quake and slide had had their way.

What could have gone through the mind of a 39-year-old wife and mother of four children as she lay there through the night, intermittently regaining consciousness alone with no sign or sound of any of her family?

She remembered little between "being in water" and waking "pinned under a tree" at dawn. Perhaps endurance of trauma can be kind, helping block pain and anxiety through the long waiting sometimes required by circumstances.

So what happened?

Various survivors at the edge of the slide describe a gigantic surge of air and river water displaced as the mountain split apart and slid down into the canyon bottom, onto and beyond the river and campground, up the other side.

This force scattered the Bennett family. The actual rocks, earth, and trees tumbling in the slide may never have touched them, only the hard blast of soft elements. Who could know how Irene became pinned by the tree?

Slide mass dammed the river and by morning the water Irene had remembered around her had drained away, leaving the riverbed downstream from the slide not dry, but exposed.

Irene thought she may have called to her family before, "and did a lot of praying," but definitely remembered calling out at daylight — "and he answered me."

It was Phil. His voice was a blessing to her.

"We crawled to each other, on the riverbed. He had seen the car. . .and that's what he was headed for when I called and he answered. I have no idea of time.

"Phil's leg was just a mess — it looked like the letter 'S' — when I found him."

Later that morning, rescue crews entered the canyon from below and found Irene and Phil. Before their evacuation, rescuers also found the body of Pud, not far away. One by one, over the next several days, searchers found the bodies of the other three children, one almost a mile downstream. The coroner's report said they all had drowned.

That first search crew included Dr. Ronald Losee of Ennis, Montana, a noted orthopedic surgeon. The mother and son were placed in the back of a pick-up truck and driven to Madison Valley Hospital in Ennis, where Dr. Losee cared for them, Irene for a month, and Phil for 47 days. Phil was in traction with a broken collar bone and multiple leg fractures. Irene remembered a nurse saying she and her son did not have a single spot on their bodies free of scrapes, bruises, skin tears or broken bones.

Irene thought the world of Dr. Losee, who spent that first night in the hospital at Phil's bedside. He took them out for a steak dinner when Phil had to return for a new leg cast, and stayed in touch with the family over the years.

The broken bones and scrapes were the easy part. How do you reconstruct a life, having endured a night during which two-thirds of your family was swept away from you and you survived?

"I sensed a caring God and said, 'Why do you think He saved us? Perhaps some day we'll know,'" she wrote a few years ago, looking back on her experiences after visiting the tragic site in 1999.

For Irene, her survival strategy began the winter after the quake, not, she said, when she was "crawling across the riverbed."

She decided to follow her long-time dream of being a teacher and enrolled in college, North Idaho College in Coeur d'Alene. It had been twenty-two years since she had finished high school. She had some insurance money. Beta Sigma Phi sorority invited her to tea and awarded her a grant of financial assistance. She did better than she had expected on entrance exams. Some of her classmates turned out to be former friends of her oldest daughter, Carole.

It took Irene until 1972 to finish college, at the University of Idaho in Moscow. She taught in the third through sixth grades for 15 years, and loved reading to her children. "We often laughed and cried together over stories," she recalled. "I'll never forget reading *Where the Red Fern Grows* by Wilson Rawls. It's a story of a boy and his dogs. The children loved it and begged each day for one more chapter … "

It's no wonder Irene and her students loved it, through their tears. A boy, Billy, fulfills a dream by saving money to buy two hound pups. The three of them survive various close calls with wild animals and Ozark nature. But in an encounter with a catamount, one of the dogs sustains fatal injuries while protecting the boy. The other hound, brooding over loss of her companion, loses her will to live and dies lying beside his grave. Later in the spring, before moving away, Billy visits the dogs' graves one last time. He finds a red fern growing over them, as happens in the legend of two Native American children found frozen to death in a snow storm. It was said that a red fern's seed could be planted only by an angel.

While Irene prepared to teach, son Phil finished high school and went on to a computer school in Arizona. He landed a job with Boeing and made his 34-year career in the Seattle plant, raising three daughters, and now fully enjoying his seven grandchildren.

Not long after starting work on her degree, Irene was invited to a New Year's Eve party and there bumped into a man she had dated back in high school, Jack Dunn. After graduation they went their separate ways. Jack was now a bachelor farmer. After meeting again they dated, cautiously, for Jack was sensitive to her loss of family. Irene and Jack were married in June 1961.

"I was very fortunate to find him because I'm a person who just really dislikes being alone," Irene said. "Jack has been real good in helping me get over it."

Asked what she makes of her being spared while losing three children and a husband, Irene relies on her faith in God.

"I'm sure that I had many, many questions, but my faith in God just gave me the feeling that this is what he had planned. I think he has all our lives planned and we don't really have that much control," she says, pausing before continuing.

"I prayed for all of them and I, of course, would love to have had more of them survive, but that wasn't the way it was, so... even though it was very hard to accept, I accepted it."

Could it have been God's plan that some are spared and others die?

"That I don't know," she says. "That's God's ... " Her voice trails off. "God knows but we don't."

Husband Jack has no doubt about why Irene was spared. It was to save his life.

Eight years after their marriage, Jack fell onto the concrete floor of his cattle shed from the hayloft above. A day or two earlier, he joked, his fall would have been broken by a huge pile of manure, but he'd already cleaned it up and spread it over his fields.

When Jack didn't come in for supper, Irene called and called, finally walking up to the barn. She found him conscious but unable to get up and bleeding from one ear. Later, doctors found broken ribs and others torn from the sternum. He had skull fractures, neck and shoulder injuries, a broken wrist and paralysis down one side.

Said Jack: "Since Pud had died and if I hadn't been married to her, I would be dead now, too. I think that's just a coincidence, I guess, I don't know ... that he died and gave me my life, really."

Irene called son Phil and he came immediately from Seattle, but not before telling a friend, "I don't know what I'll do with my mother if she loses another person."

But when he arrived Jack had improved and, as Irene recalled the moment, through her tears she added, "The Lord has heard our prayers lots of times."

Irene feared storms the rest of her life, especially wind sounds, and "anything that shakes. I had a friend who kept

25

asking me to come to her house to relax in her vibrating rocker. She thought that would be so restful. She didn't know what that did to me. It was just like going through the thing all over again." She laughed at herself.

When Phil still was in high school and living at home, Irene recalled, "If he was away and a wind would come up, he would immediately come home because he knew I was afraid."

Phil had revisited the slide several times before he was able to convince Irene to go. That was for the quake's 40th anniversary, in 1999. It was her first meeting with other survivors.

"Phil insisted that I go back" Irene said. "After a number of years really it was good. I was glad I went."

The trip also provided a catharsis allowing her to write her book, *Out of the Night*. "One of my teacher friends convinced me to write it. It's a labor of love. It took me a long time, and my son helped, but it was a difficult thing to do."

But for this book, Phil at first declined to be interviewed: "I'm not interested. I've gone on with my life and it's one of those things I'm not interested in doing." Irene wasn't surprised.

Nearly three years later, just before this book went to press, I decided to try Phil again. He responded, cautiously at first then more freely, admitting, "You caught me at the right time."

Phil had no sense of time that night when he awoke feeling cold, feeling "pushed, like being hit by a freight liner or whatever … power unbelievable, then water came down and pushed into trees and rocks and my body … cold, cold, cold … total daze … tried to stand but my leg was broken … dust rolled up around the moon … earth shook … wind blew very hard … after water receded I dug a hole and covered myself with dirt —

26

Scout training …called out — I think, as though a dream — but a kid of 16 may not know."

Phil told a close friend about spending the night, covered with mud and gravel, hearing rocks roll down slopes to his left, then his right, wondering when a next one might hit him

I asked about his first thoughts at dawn after the quake, none of his family in sight.

"I remember wondering, "Why me? What's this mean for me?"'

The only thing that looked familiar to him at first light was the family's 1956 Chevrolet station wagon, "crushed and laying on the riverbed, its license plate, part of my life …

"I tried to walk … I crawled … I'm going to get emotional now …no clue where Mom was … going toward the car, she from the far side, carrying my belt. She clung to the only thing she had found of any of us … asking each other 'Are you OK? Where's the family?'"

I asked if he could see the slide or understand what had happened.

"No, and didn't try. It was just survival. The earth was still shaking. We're in mud and muck, cold and naked … It was two or three days before they told me the rest were dead, that they had found their bodies." That night and morning were such a daze Phil still is disoriented as to directions, distances and locations when he revisits the place.

"I believed my Mom and I had other goals in life," Phil muses as he recalls that August night 50 years before, somewhat surprised at himself for venturing so deeply into memories.

"Have I found mine? I don't know." But he seems not to be upset by any uncertainty.

What brought the Bennett family to the Madison River canyon that night? Irene just remembered having two children in their late teens and wanting a family vacation before they left home.

I asked her about the nature of her prayers during that long night — alone, naked, separated from her family, wet and cold, pinned under that tree, the fractured mountain looming over her, its horizon outlined in the moonlight. Irene said she recited the 121st Psalm over and over, its text and her experience exemplifying the irony and paradox of religious faith:

I lift up my eyes to the hills. From whence does my help come? My help comes from the Lord, who made heaven and earth. He will not let your foot be moved, he who keeps you will not slumber. Behold, he who keeps Israel will neither slumber nor sleep. The Lord is your keeper; the Lord is your shade on your right hand. The sun shall not smite you by day, nor the moon by night. The Lord will keep you from all evil; he will keep your life. The Lord will keep your going out and your coming in from this time forth and for evermore.

Irene and Jack lived for forty-six years in a small farm home on a hillside overlooking the town where they first met, attended school, and courted — Hope, Idaho. Irene died in April 2007, just one year after being interviewed for this story. Jack died at age 88 in June 2008, 11 days after his tractor rolled over and crushed him while he cultivated the garden on their farm.

Chapter 7

LOSEE: "Huffin', Puffin' and Comin' Out of It"

Dr. Ronald E. Losee — who left Dartmouth College and Yale University Medical School to come west — takes great pride in being a "country doc" in the best sense of the word, but also having a substantial orthopedic reputation as a knee specialist.

Irene Bennett and her son Phillip were among his first patients after returning to Montana from a two-year orthopedic surgery residency at the Royal Victoria Hospital in Montreal.

On the night of the quake, Losee and his wife Olive, a nurse, had driven 100 miles home to Ennis after performing surgery at the state institution for developmentally disabled persons in Boulder, Montana: "No sooner had we reached home than the siren blew. Someone in the middle of the street said the dam's going to break. Next thing we know we see pickup trucks going 'round and 'round in circles loaded with refrigerators and their wife's clothing and stuff hanging out. They didn't know what to do. Where do we go now? They had visions of a great flood with the Hebgen Dam going.

"The whole town gathered up on the hill. Bartenders brought all the booze they had — it was one helluva good night. Up all night, our kids and all, havin' a good time.

"Nothing happened."

At dawn, sleepless, Losee was summoned by Fish and Game Department officers who flew him in a small plane up to the Staggers Ranch area on the Madison River, less than a mile below the slide but not within sight of it because of a turn in the canyon walls.

"I hated airplanes," he recalls. "As we took off I thought now's as good a time as any. I was lookin' down and there was not much water in the river. What the hell is this? A guy's fishing there. Hey, there's going to be a great flood. He must not have heard about the dam. Or the fishing must have been good because the fish were concentrated in holes.

"What was this? Your brains don't work. Nothing works.

"We landed on the road. There were these two people there with their strange story. We had to get them help.

"I didn't want anyone to drive me. I wanted to control that truck in case there was a flood of water. I kept looking back. Irene and Phillip were lying in the back of the pickup. There were rocks in the road; I could tell you now just where they were. We finally got to the hospital. The boy had a compound fracture. We put his leg together with what we had."

Olive's nursing skills meanwhile were pressed into service by being flown in a second Fish and Game plane to another site, Cliff Lake. In her words, "The pilot flew around a little bit and landed on the road. There was somebody under a big rock, just the feet sticking out. They were dead."

Realizing the futility of their mission, the petite nurse concluded wistfully, "I couldn't lift that damn rock!"

Back at the hospital in Ennis, it was noon before Losee learned of the rockslides and their human toll. "What bothers me is why I didn't know what had made the water stop," he fusses as he remembers that day.

"As an orthopedic surgeon you've seen much trauma," I said. "What does the typical victim do? Is there any pattern?"

"No," he answers.

"Their opinion of the Creator is the essence of chance … thank God we made it. Why do you ask?"

I explained my interest in survival — human experience interfacing with nature's forces, overwhelming personal trauma juxtaposed against an unimaginable, hostile environment.

"No, I don't see that, people putting a lot of interpretation on survival. Usually it's animal stuff — just breathin', huffin' and puffin' and comin' out of it," he tells me. "Now when you get the religious thing into it, that may come later."

For those first days, Losee says, Irene could not explain what had happened — "and if she explained it, I didn't receive it." Irene continued to hold out hope that the other four members of her family would be found alive.

"Irene's story was so intense. That's a core story — a core story," Losee muses 50 years later.

"It was something no one's ever experienced before, and they don't know how to talk about it."

Chapter 8

Visitors at the Slide Stand in Awe

No matter which way you approach, the final ascent up to the Earthquake Lake Visitor Center is a barren scene. The Center is on a huge pile of rocks. During nearly 50 years, very little vegetation has taken root. You stand on 80 million tons of stone that once clung to the north-facing mountain ridge to the south.

It takes some time, as you gaze south to that immense mountain scar, to fathom that the rock material that once was "up there" is now below and in front of you damming the Madison River, under you at the 230-foot height of the slide, and above and behind you as the leading edge of the slide rode 400 feet up the north side of the canyon. And all that material moved as a mass in just a few seconds.

Unless you've heard the story, you have absolutely no clue that somewhere below you are the bodies of 19 persons believed to be buried where they slept in or near the old Rock Creek Campground. Part of the campground is under the slide, part of it covered by waters of Earthquake Lake, which started forming the instant the slide came down. Dead trees, now gray skeletons, sprout from the lake where they once bordered the free-flowing Madison River.

Joanne Girvin is a cheery woman, a 17-year Forest Service employee who, as an information officer, has supervised Visitor Center operations since 1990. She cackles with laughter as I observe, "You work at this rock pile day after day. . ." and then I continue, "like being in prison. What's the impact of looking at that mountain every day, wondering if it could happen again? What does it mean to you?"

The Center clearly rests in the slide zone.

"A lot of people ask me whether I feel safe here," Joanne says.

"I do. As far as that landslide goes, you know, the pressure that produced the earthquake has released. However, I've experienced landslides from the other side of the canyon and they were probably due to a wet spring and that can still happen.

"Seventeen summers, and I've never felt an earthquake here. I have in West Yellowstone and along Hebgen Lake. I felt earthquakes there." A seismograph in the Center occasionally records squiggles but they're usually signs of heavy equipment moving along the highway below.

But what about the immensity of it all?

"You approach the slide from below, from the west, that's when it still to this day really hits me like wow, that's a huge landslide, versus coming the other way when I watch the cormorants in the lake and the eagles and it's kind of serene coming to work.

"Early in the season," Joanne says, "I take a lot of school groups up the slide to the boulder and its plaque commemorating the dead (Figs. 1 and 56). They just can't believe that those two boulders were once on the other side of the river canyon."

Those dolomite boulders were part of a ledge, a buttress that runs horizontally along the lower part of the ridge. Above the stronger dolomite were layers of schist and gneiss, both much less stable material, weakened by a long period of weathering and lying at an angle poised to slide downhill if provoked.

I asked two geologists who authored technical papers on the 1959 quake and the area's ancient geologic history whether that mountainside was known to be a potential hazard pre-August 1959. Irving J. Witkind, now deceased, and Warren Hamilton, both PhDs retired from the U. S. Geological Survey, gave similar answers: The known geology of the mountainside indicated the possibility of instability — plus, it was in an active earthquake zone — but no one had tagged it as a hazard.

"It was not loose material waiting to slough off," Hamilton said. "But with hindsight, it became very obvious why it slid." Potentially hazardous areas such as these are treated today in a much more systematic manner.

As for how we examine and tolerate risk, some of the most intensive and expensive urbanization in the United States is built atop this country's most active earthquake zone, the San Andreas fault running along the California coast, both onshore and off. People live with the risks.

Second in quake activity is this Yellowstone-Hebgen intersection of Montana, Wyoming and Idaho. But in comparison with California, this is the wide open spaces, even considering the 3 million visitors annually traveling to the national park.

This mass of suddenly-shifted material forms the dam across the Madison River and resembles a saddle across the canyon. It appears somewhat out of place, yet in the mountain West one gets used to encountering unexpected landshapes. Stark, broken rock of all shapes and sizes, devoid of vegetation, edges up to green forest, both at the leading northern prow of the slide and along its flanks on the south ridge from whence it fell. It's not unlike steep talus slopes visible almost anywhere there are mountains — jumbled rock slopes whose irregular

boulders have fallen from rock cliffs higher up, usually just weathering out to fall until finding some slope niche in which to defy gravity in their new angle of repose. Thus the title of Wallace Stegner's 1972 Pulitzer-winning novel, *The Angle of Repose.* A rock pile or a sand pile will tend to stack up with its own angle of repose. The slope angle is a function of the pile particles' density, size, surface area, and coefficient of friction.

Breaking of the dolomite's restraining buttress as a result of the earthquake upset this balance and the slide stopped only after reaching a new angle of repose.

Joanne is not surprised when visitors ask whether she has doubts about coming up here every day of the summer. The scarred mountain appears as if it could slide again

In 2007, visitors on the slide's anniversary date, Aug. 17, had a treat when two survivors of the quake and slide, Bonnie Schreiber, and her mother, Germaine Holmes Schreiber, stopped by and were met by a television reporter and cameraman from Bozeman, Montana, a hundred miles away. As the interview proceeded, Bonnie's story-telling drew a crowd and a hearty round of applause at the end.

Jim Field of Portage, Wisconsin, remembers visiting nearby Yellowstone National Park as a child five years after the quake and slide, but his family did not realize it was something to see.

He looks with me now at the rock rubble covering the canyon bottom, contemplating the campers buried there: "How could they have known what was happening?" he asks.

Geologists are uncertain about the time lag, if any, between the quake and the start of the slide. Survivors give varying estimates. But reliable calculations peg the slide's speed at 100 miles per hour.

"I guess it could happen again, huh?" Jim says, half asking. "Interesting. I'm glad we could stop. We were just cruising down from the park and wanted to take a break when we happened to see the sign."

This visitors' center is a life-transforming experience, different from most tourist stops.

Allen and Joan Sharp of Great Falls have known of the quake and slide most of their lives, felt it from many miles away. They looked out on the slide debris her father had helped re-shape. For days he had transported heavy equipment to the site as crews feverishly worked to create a stable spillway over the slide.

"Families would come up with license plate numbers" trying to find some trace of missing campers, she said. "Dad said it was just heart-wrenching." One man dug at the downstream, dry side of the slide for days, searching for his missing daughter.

A silver-haired woman with a beautiful smile lingers with her friend after viewing the Forest Service video, gazing out the huge windows offering a panorama of the split mountain.

"I live in the area and I come here all the time," she said. "It happened the year I graduated from college, so it was a significant time in my life.

"My fiancé was over here in Montana somewhere — I didn't know where — with his family on vacation. It didn't occur to him that I might be worried.

"I love to come up here," she says, somewhat self-consciously. "I bring everyone who comes to visit us." She wished to speak anonymously.

What is it that intrigues her?

"For me," she said, "it's the tragedy to all the people and the changes it brought."

Her uncle and aunt attended a wedding in Livingston, Montana, a day before the quake and the newlyweds were to have camped at Rock Creek on their honeymoon. She said no one is known to have heard from them ever again.

Other people are known to have planned to camp at Rock Creek that night but, for some reason, or set of reasons, drove on.

"We never know what those reasons are, do we?" the first woman asked.

"I don't know that earthquakes happen for reasons other than geological, but … " Her voice trails off.

To view the remnants of the Madison Canyon earthquake and slide is to view a slice in time. The event, however, initiated a range of human emotions — from the joy of being spared, to the grief of knowing those who were not — lasting for untold years, even generations.

The meanings these survivors applied to the event were quite varied, but presumably appropriate for each.

And as long-lasting as these meanings may be in making sense of life and death, they are but a brief moment in the seemingly neutral and detached overall earth history involved.

Few other experiences so effectively show the fleeting interface of human choice and existence with the billions of years and stages of earth creation which made the moment possible.

It happened in the blink of an eye, but in a time dimensional context that stretches our comprehension beyond the ordinary.

The scarred mountainside still sheds numerous small rock falls and slides, according to Kelly Galloup, who runs the Slide

Inn fly-fishing shop not far downstream and often drives over the slide. He notes that there are some hardy souls not intimidated by the steep terrain. In winter he sees skiers struggling up the tree-free slope for the exhilarating plunge back down.

Chapter 9

Camped on Top of It

Imagine two geologists camped in southwestern Montana, near the end of their summer field work gathering data for the U. S. Geological Survey, being roused in the middle of the night by the largest earthquake they'd ever likely experience. They were right on top of it. How would they react?

Pretty much just like anyone.

In this case it was Irving J. Witkind, PhD, in one camp trailer and his assistant, Jack Epstein, MS, and Jack's wife Anita in the other. Jack's 13-year-old brother, Harvey, had a tent. See Figs. 13 and 14.

A poker game was underway in the Epstein trailer. Being 10 years older had not helped Jack beat his brother, who was visiting the camp for a few days. Jack was down $40 (years later Harvey would be banned from at least one Las Vegas casino for being too good at mathematics, i.e., counting cards) and Jack wanted to recover his losses before the kid left. The earthquake erased all that, Jack remembers with a laugh almost 50 years later. Suddenly there was no time for poker.

Anita and Harvey run outside and meet the always serious Dr. Witkind standing in his pajamas. Jack tries to catch the gasoline lantern whirling round on its ceiling hook. The ground is rolling and pitching beneath them. Someone hopefully suggests it might be just "a minor event."

First the earth's shaking and then, from some unknown but distant place, came a huge roar.

Witkind later wrote to his wife: " … I thought that the trailer had somehow come off its jacks, jumped the chocks, and was rolling down the hill. I scrambled out the front door determined to stop the trailer, no matter what, although I had no idea as to how I would go about it. When I got outside, the trailer was in place, but the trees were whipping back and forth and the leaves were rustling as if moved by a strong wind — but there was no wind. I knew right then that it was an earthquake. I could hear avalanches in the canyons behind me, and could see huge clouds of dust billow out of the canyon mouths … "

Jack's wife wrote: "All of a sudden the trailer began to shake violently up and down and back and forth … I saw water pouring out of the wash basin. All dishes, groceries and clothes were falling out of the cabinets, and the gasoline lantern hanging from the ceiling swinging in a 2-foot circle which, if it had fallen, would have set the whole trailer on fire. There were fantastic rumblings. The farthest thing from my mind was an earthquake. In this same split second I thought that the 100-pound propane tank outside the trailer was starting to explode … In pure horror and fright I dashed out the door and screamed for everyone to follow and run as far away from the trailer as possible. Jack was still in the trailer, trying to stop the lantern. He got beaned on the head with it, gave up, and came charging out. He had realized from the first that it was a quake. My complete horror came after I hit the ground and found that it was no better than in the trailer. The solid earth, 'terra firma,' was like a glob of jelly. I was frantic — there was nowhere to get away from the fantastic sensation. Jack screamed not to run near the woods because trees were toppling all over … "

They were located about three miles from the epicenter of the quake — seismic analysis later relocated it and changed its magnitude (see area map, inside front cover) — and amazingly close to a major fault scarp, near the Duck Creek junction of Highways 191 and 287.

Their base camp for the summer was about a quarter mile up slope from Blarneystone Ranch buildings, then owned by the Culligan family of soft-water fame. The survey party's hasty, midnight Jeep ride to the ranch was suddenly cut short (Figs. 17 and 18), about 2 feet shy of a steep drop-off where all summer they had ascended and descended an unusually steep part of the hill. In fact they had thought the steep incline indicated the profile of an old stream terrace, its shape softened by erosion, gravity and other effects of time.

But now it was a cliff more than 10 feet high, and later found to be near the eastern end of the Red Canyon fault scarp, an old but revived earth fracture, a scar that indeed had been smoothed over by time.

Leaving the Jeep, they scrambled down the scarp in the dark to reach the Blarneystone headquarters, finding some of it intact, some of it in shambles. One large building (Fig. 19) unknowingly had been built astride the hidden fault. The portion of the building on subsiding ground was damaged but remained largely intact, while the portion left on high ground was completely flattened.

"A Catholic priest was a Culligan guest that night," recalls Wit, as he is called by colleagues and friends. "I thought we'd better get people out of there before the place completely collapsed. I urged the priest to leave. 'Let me get my shoes and pants on,' he said. I was screaming, 'No, you've got to get out now.'"

Outside, people — and chickens — were bewildered. "The chickens," Jack recalls, "got loose and were running around. A ranch hand picked one up and it laid an egg in his hand."

Wit says he had never experienced an earthquake before or since, "But I knew what this one was — everything fit."

They spent the night and the next day checking on people and their experiences, trying to help wherever possible.

One of the first places Wit and Jack checked was a fault area they had explored the day of the quake. Their horse trail crossed the hidden fault. Retracing, they found the trail — just like back at their camp road — was split by the new fault scarp, a drop of about 15 feet from top to bottom. It had been a relatively smooth trail the day before.

It was Wit's second year in the area. "We had the geology pretty much resolved. We had determined the structural pattern which later was crucial to understanding the quake. Quakes had happened tens of thousands of times before, and will happen tens of thousands of times again." Wit thought ground displacement of 10 to 20 feet was typical for the numerous prehistoric Hebgen-area quakes.

"The problem is prediction," he said. "To a certain extent it's better to tell what happened rather than to predict."

As we talked, Wit idly sketched. "Rocks overturn, then fault (fracture) through here. In essence it is movement along a fault that causes a quake. It is a chattering bump bump down." These were normal faults, one side of the split dropping, the other remaining at the same elevation, or rising. Displacement in a strike-slip fault, like San Andreas along the Pacific coast, is horizontal, left or right.

Asked about their surveying the Kirkwood Ridge only days before its fracture, Jack said, "We, of course, did not think that there would be a fault and earthquake developing along Kirkwood Ridge. But our mapping prior to the earthquake did show that there was a normal, down-dropped fault to account for our mapping.

"The fact that the fault scarp developed along Kirkwood confirmed our mapping. As a matter of fact, that is one of the areas where Wit and I had a conversation about the structure, and I think he commented about that to you in your interview with him." Indeed, he had.

What attracts a New York City youngster to geology? Wit blamed his father. "He would come back from work on Friday nights and we'd pack the car — my mother hated it — and we'd go into the Catskills. Perhaps some of that smeared off on me," said the 90-year-old, offering me a cola at his kitchen table in southeastern suburban Denver. "It's been a wonderful life."

Wit attended Brooklyn College — "the poor man's Harvard" — then received a master's degree at Columbia University. He made major in the Army and after World War II combat in Germany earned his doctorate at the University of Colorado. He chose the U. S. Geological Survey at a third of what a private oil company would pay him because, while at Columbia, Texaco had fired their entire geology staff and he didn't want to risk that.

Of all his work for the USGS in Montana and elsewhere, Wit is proudest of his study of the role of salt in the structural development of central Utah.

"As I look back, the Yellowstone quake was a wonderful experience for me," he said. "I don't think it did much for my career but it left me with a wealth of knowledge."

As a boy, because of appendicitis which altered his school activities, Jack turned to reading. He got so hooked on dinosaurs that he learned the names of about 50, and eventually majored in geology, also at Brooklyn College. He worked two summers in the Black Hills of South Dakota while earning his MS at the University of Wyoming before his assignment in Montana. Jack worked out of West Yellowstone for about a month after the quake. There was snow on the ground when he was transferred to 95-degree heat in Louisiana to study fluctuations of ground water. He later earned his doctorate at Ohio State University, his dissertation based on a Pennsylvania geological mapping project.

Jack and Anita had driven from Denver in a government Jeep, pulling a 300-gallon water tank to the field site near West Yellowstone. Jack's job was to assist Wit, help with safety, maintain and fuel the vehicles, and wrangle their three horses. "We were one of the few USGS parties that used horses. When I had to drive the Jeep into West Yellowstone for water, Anita and I would catch a movie while filling the water tank." Funny what details Jack remembers now from his home in Virginia.

"Wit was a very serious person," Jack says both descriptively and respectfully. "Both of us grew up in New York City. He would say 'do this' and I would say 'why.'

I could deal with him professionally and Wit recognized that."

"Jack was an extraordinarily bright young man," Wit recalled. "I remember working with Jack back in the mountains before the quake. We were standing about here (pointing to his sketch on the kitchen table). We tried several ideas, this or that. I was sketching in my book.

"One of us said it must have been a case of this having once been together, then it dropped. And I said, 'That is it, that's it.'

If you find Madison limestone at two levels 1,000 feet apart, you know they were once together" — the moment of truth Jack referred to above.

Dr. Witkind was the sole or lead author of five of the 20 technical papers published by USGS in 1964 as *The Hebgen Lake, Montana, Earthquake of Aug. 17, 1959: Geological Survey Professional Paper 435*, made up of 242 pages of photographs, maps, diagrams, statistical tables, measurements, professional and lay observations, analyses, hypotheses — mostly aimed at understanding what goes on underneath by studying the surface.

Another of the geologists involved was Warren Hamilton who disagreed sharply with Witkind's interpretation of the data. *Paper 435* carries both theories.

At the end of my interview with Wit, he said, "We would like to remain detached and objective. There is much evidence since then. I'm sure evidence supports my side but you need to talk to the other side. Warren lives close by, a few miles on the other side of Denver. There are very few of us left.

"Warren is a very prestigious geologist. We never worked together. We exchanged some very tough words about the interpretation. Never friends, but acquaintances. But he's top notch, a very bright mind. You ought to talk with him."

What a gracious, fair-minded thing to do, I thought. Here was a man dedicated to honest, open scientific inquiry, even when there is sharp disagreement.

And with that Wit chuckled, saying how he used to come home distraught about some technical issue and his wife couldn't understand why he was so upset: "She didn't understand you become emotionally involved in these things. I think I've calmed down quite a bit, a great bit."

Later, when I interviewed Jack about that night in Montana, I asked if professionally he hadn't thought the quake was a great gift that had fallen right in his lap — a beginning geologist finding himself thrust into the middle of one of the most dramatic and mysterious of all geologic phenomena, the earth shaking under and all around him, probably a once-in-several-lifetimes kind of experience.

"I felt excited by it, but not like Wit felt," Jack says. "We went down the next day to see the fault scarp we had almost driven over. When he saw it I remember him looking up, spreading his arms and saying, 'It's mine, it's mine!'"

It was a geologist's version of "territorial imperative."

Jack acknowledges there were strong differences between his boss and the Myers/Hamilton team. He laughed: "You put ten geologists out in the field, and you get ten interpretations of what they've seen." Another rock veteran laughed at that observation and said, "Maybe more like fifteen."

"What is so neat about geology is," Jack continued, "if you look at the earth — measure rocks, try to figure out what they're doing underneath the soil covering — the percentage of rocks that are actually exposed at the surface may be less than half of one percent … So you have a lot of information but it's not complete.

"You have to base your interpretations on your past experiences, which are also varied. The subjects in geology range to chemistry and physics and geophysics and paleontology and math and computer things and modeling and structural geology and surficial geology and geomorphology.

"When plate tectonics hit in the middle '60s we all argued a lot about it." Jack referred to an all-encompassing theory that geology is controlled by large continental plates of the earth's crust that are always on the move. In contrast was a more local view of rock movement, as that producing earthquakes along relatively small fault lines, quite different from the massive movement of plates.

"Now very few geologists would argue against it," he continues. "It's such a unifying theory."

What is the lasting image of the Hebgen quake that comes back to Jack? It's about the movement of time and how we experience change.

Jack told of watching a large boulder bounding down a mountainside in the days following the quake, scarring stationary rocks as it fell. His epiphany was that sudden, often catastrophic events — scarred rocks, fault scarps, landslides, whole lakes being tilted out of kilter — are different only in duration from longer-term geologic processes. The principle of uniformitarianism may be a long-held view of gradual earth-building processes, but it may also include these pulses of instantaneous events. At Hebgen, Jack was seeing both.

He was reminded of a presentation years ago by USGS geologist Gene Shoemaker. He had gone to the Grand Canyon for the 100th anniversary of a famous photograph taken there, where the rock layers are stacked in chronological sequence for anyone to see. Gene wanted to check how time might have affected the scene. Using the old photograph for comparison in one segment, he could not find a single rock that had moved. In other spots, erosion had changed the picture radically.

"Gene died in Australia driving down a back road," Jack said, "hit head-on by the only other vehicle within miles."

"With that one falling boulder," he continued, "it hit me that the earth is constantly in motion. No place in this world is it completely stable."

Irving Witkind died in February 2008 a month shy of his 91st birthday, before a third interview for this book could be arranged.

Fig. 1—Big as a house, this boulder was carried with other dolomitic rock debris from the far mountainside, down into the Madison River Canyon and 400 feet up this north side of the canyon. It seems almost to have "floated" here as the initiating Hebgen Lake earthquake caused such a gravitational change that rock material with slide potential literally took on fluid characteristics and flowed down, and then up. The boulder shows no scrapes or other signs of tumbling. Delicate, rock-clinging lichen were found unscathed by the ride.
— Author's photo

Fig. 2—Looking northwest, the West Yellowstone Basin and Hebgen Lake are pictured and constitute the entire scene except for the sky and the snowy Madison Range receding northward on the horizon. Horse Butte, at the far end of the land area protruding into the bottom of the picture, divides the upper end of Hebgen from its inlet sources — the Grayling Arm on the right, the Madison Arm on the left — flowing out of Yellowstone National Park. Hebgen fault scarp runs along the north shoreline, right side, but is not clearly visible. It starts just beyond the peninsula nearly crossing Grayling Arm and ends just beyond Hebgen Dam at the far end of the lake. A companion fracture, the Red Canyon fault, produced the scarp parallel to and not far below Kirkwood Ridge, top right corner. Relationship between the near-shore Hebgen fault scarp and the Red Canyon scarp, high on Kirkwood Ridge, is demonstrated in Fig. 25.

— Photo by Doug Chapman, Montana Aircraft, Inc.

43

Fig. 3—Turning back, you look southeast toward West Yellowstone, Montana. You see Hebgen Lake's Madison Arm, right, and the Grayling Arm on the left. Much of the flat horizon is made up of basalt formations that flowed up from the south, 70,000 or more years old. Most of that horizon lies within the western side of Yellowstone National Park, extending south and west of West Yellowstone. At the bottom, you see Hebgen Dam and the Madison River flowing to the right. The river loops around a spur of predominantly dolomite. — Chapman photo

Fig. 4—From above Hebgen Dam, looking southeast as the Madison River cuts through the canyon dividing the Madison Range, right, from the Henry's Lake Mountains, left. Barely visible at the far end of Earthquake Lake is the 230-foot-deep pile of rock debris that tumbled down from the left, the snow-covered patch at the canyon's mouth. Near the center of the picture is a triangle-shaped section of high ground, bounded on the left by the river and on the right by Highway 287. Campers flocked to it in the night, realizing it was the only readily accessible flat ground in the canyon that was safe from the rising river — dammed by the slide — and from possible release of water from Hebgen Lake should the old dam fail. The dam, built in 1915, sustained cracks up to six inches wide but still stands today.

— Chapman photo

Fig.5—THE SLIDE!!! These aerial photos were made in October after a dusting of snow, which actually highlights the rocky scar made by the slide. Earthquake Lake is 190 feet deep at this point. Without it and the slide mass, the Madison River would drop at a more leisurely pace from the canyon mouth into the broad Madison Valley beyond. For days after the quake and slide, engineers worked feverishly to create a stable spillway through the slide and avoid sudden erosion and flooding of Ennis, Montana, 44 miles downstream. On the slide, a visitor center and parking lot are visible near Highway 287. Visible on the valley floor are terraces marking old river meanders.

— Chapman photo

46

Fig.6—The latent Madison Fault lies along the base of mountains receding into the distance from the slide area. It has fractured numerous times in pre-historic times but showed very little deformation in the 1959 Hebgen quake. It's in a high potential quake zone (see Fig. 50) and likely accumulated more fault-producing stress from Hebgen's movement. A satellite photo of Madison Fault is reproduced as Fig. 48. The fault runs for 40 miles, mostly north and south, along the base of the pictured Henry's Lake Mountains, formerly considered part of the Madison Range which trends north to the right and out of the picture. Highway 87 rises toward Raynolds Pass in the distance. Some geologists believe the Madison River, before it cut through the canyon at left, flowed south from the West Yellowstone Basin, coming around the far end of these Henry's Lake Mountains and across the upper right corner of this scene into the valley.

— Chapman photo

Fig. 7—Bonnie Schrieber, right, was one of the first persons interviewed for this book. She and her mother, Germaine Holmes Schreiber, both survivors of the quake and slide, are pictured in the Forest Service visitor center atop the Madison slide in August 2008, after Bonnie drew a crowd of tourists overhearing her speaking with a television reporter.

— Author's photo

Fig. 8—John Owen's family often rented a cabin to fish in the Madison Canyon, and that summer he was 15. They were about four miles from the slide area when the quake hit at 11:37 p.m. Not knowing of the slide — hearing only the thunderous roar — John's family and others wondered whether the Cold War had heated up.

— Author's photo

Fig. 9—Mildred "Tootie" Greene, her late husband Ramon, and son Steve, like others, did not get the campsite of their choice at Rock Creek, which was lucky. Tootie had experience as a hospital nurse but realized when others around her signed up for Red Cross first-aid training, that she should, too, to be prepared for outdoor misadventures. Good choice. She finished just a month before their trip to the Madison Canyon. This snapshot was made soon after they returned home.

— Family photo

Fig. 10—The Ost family, of Queens, New York, camped at Rock Creek ready to head for Yellowstone National Park the next day. The four siblings got together with their parents on instinct, just six weeks before their father died, and the family posed for this photo: The Rev. Elmer and Ruth Ost and, from left, Susan, Joan, Jerre and Larry.

— Family photo

Fig. 11—One of the last pictures, bottom left, of Irene and Pud Bennett's children together before the Hebgen quake and slide: Phil, then 16, holding Susan, 5, with Tom, 10, and Carole, 17. Irene said later they planned the trip to Yellowstone National Park that summer because, with two teenagers, it might be their last chance for a family vacation. Years later, a new family group gathered (color photo): Phil, center, and proceeding counterclockwise, his mother Irene, her second husband Jack Dunn, Phil's wife Robin, and their daughters Riann, Amy, and Lindsay. Phil and Robin have seven grandchildren. — Family photos

Fig. 12—The Bennetts' family car, a 1956 Chevrolet station wagon, was thrown some 100 yards by the blast of air and river water displaced by the slide. Irene and Phil found themselves on opposite sides of the car when they heard each other's shouts in the morning, downstream from the slide. The rock slope that extends behind the trees is part of the slide, having collapsed from the right canyon wall, sliding across the river and up the left canyon wall. — Forest Service photo

Fig. 13—Irving J. Witkind authored many of the USGS geologic reports in its Professional Paper 435. He was in his second summer doing field work, camped near what turned out to be the epicenter of the Hebgen quake. Witkind died six months after this picture, in his home near Denver.

— Author's photo

Fig. 14—Jack B. Epstein was Witkind's assistant the summer of 1959, in his rookie year with the USGS. Jack and his wife had a camp trailer near Wit's when the quake hit. He now lives near Washington, D.C., volunteers for various special projects for the agency, and has offered much help and encouragement in production of this book.

— Author's photo

Fig. 15—The Earthquake Lake Visitor Center's supervisor, Joanne Girvin, points to a map location as she and assistant Tickie Davis help a tourist family. Through the summer season, Joanne and her staff commute daily to this mound of rock 230 feet above the old river bed, and look up to the rockslide's source towering above them.

— Author's photo

Feb. 16—Warren Hamilton was at his USGS office in Denver the morning after the Hebgen quake, and was one of the first scientists sent north to the West Yellowstone basin to study the event. Now retired, Hamilton lives not far from Denver and keeps numerous files and maps for his research and writing. He and Witkind (Fig. 13) had intense disagreement about interpreting the quake.

— Author's photo

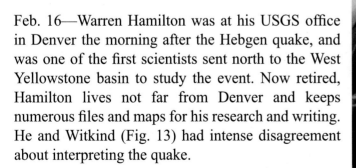

Figs. 17 and 18—Scarps are the ground surface manifestation of a fault, or fracture, in bedrock perhaps many miles below. All summer, Witkind and Epstein had driven this dirt road to their camp trailers up over the ridge, thinking the sudden rise was an old stream terrace, when in hindsight it turned out to be a pre-historic fault scarp, weathered and eroded into obscurity. Near midnight after the quake, they almost drove over the Red Canyon scarp. The quake epicenter was only a couple of miles beyond the ridge. The black and white photo shows a classic example of a graben, German for "ditch," formed when the subsiding surface of a normal fault drops down and away from the opposing surface.

— Epstein-USGS photos

Road above the fault scarp

Road below the fault scarp

SCARPS

Fig. 19—A Blarneystone Ranch building was unknowingly built across a smoothed-over Red Canyon fault line that last had fractured an estimated 1-3,000 years ago. The subsiding side survived, barely, and the upper side was flattened. Years later, after the building was removed and the scarp had weathered, new owners bulldozed the slope smooth and were unaware of the 1959 destruction in their back yard. The same fault winds up the mountainside to create the scarp shown in Fig. 23.   — Epstein-USGS photo

Fig. 20—The 1959 Hebgen fault scarp crosses this 2000 photo, indicated by the sharp drop and graben at its foot. A previous fault produced the scarp above it, 1-3,000 years before. The new scarp eventually will recede and weather smooth like the one above has done over the ages. Both result from a fault miles below. The Hebgen and the Red Canyon faults appear to fracture together as a complex fault system.

— Schwartz-USGS photo

Fig. 21—History unfolds in the soil. Geologist Schwartz and colleagues dug a trench into the Hebgen fault scarp face to expose profiles of two seismic events—material in a wedge shape that has fallen from the 1959 scarp face, and the lower material below the white zig-zag line, marked PU for penultimate event, from a quake 1-3,000 years ago. In this case, the non-subsiding slope and face (rocky soil to the right) are virtually the same for both events. A roll of green tape shows scale.   —Schwartz-USGS photo

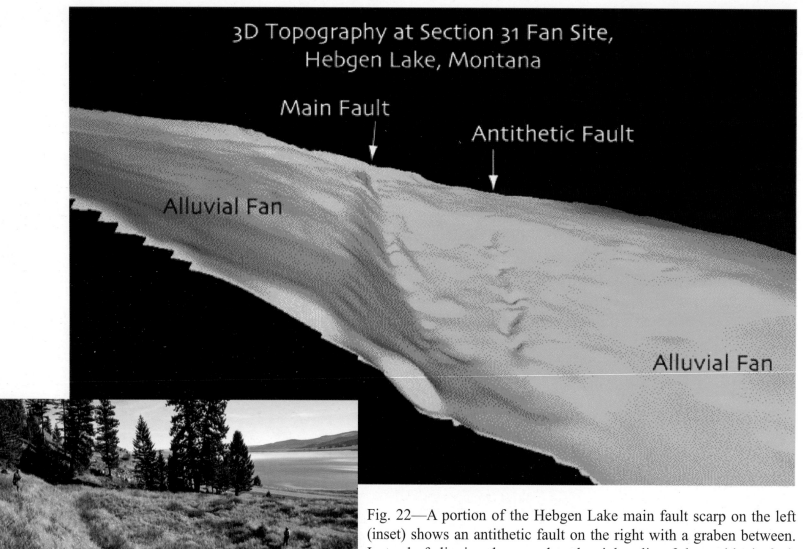

3D Topography at Section 31 Fan Site,
Hebgen Lake, Montana

Main Fault

Antithetic Fault

Alluvial Fan

Alluvial Fan

Fig. 22—A portion of the Hebgen Lake main fault scarp on the left
(inset) shows an antithetic fault on the right with a graben between.
Instead of slipping down and to the right, slip of the antithetic fault
is down and back toward the left as shown by the illustration. Scarps
are the surface manifestation, usually in loose soil, of bedrock faulting
far below. This north shoreline of Hebgen Lake and the larger West
Yellowstone basin have faulted and subsided numerous times.

—Schwartz-USGS illustrations

Fig. 23—Magestic limestone outcroppings named Kirkwood Ridge rise above and parallel to the 1959 Red Canyon fault scarp. Earth movement that produced these features is separated by more than 24 million years, the Kirkwood thrust being part of ancient mountain-building processes. Behind Kirkwood, trending northward, is the snow-capped Madison Range. This curving scarp descends off the ridge (toward the lower right corner) to Red Canyon Creek shown in Fig. 24.

— Chapman photo

Fig. 25—A common source (inset), indicated by the red line, is theorized to produce the complex fault system including the Hebgen fault, yellow, and Red Canyon, blue. The split is about 8 kilometers, or 4.8 miles, deep. Surface distance between the two scarps is about 3 miles.

--Representation started as data from Trimble and Smith, developed by Doser, later modified by Schwartz.

Fig. 24—Red Canyon fault scarp, after 50 years, provides more evidence to David Schwartz and Suzanne Hacker, right, that it is just the latest of repeated faults in this location. They are with the USGS earthquake hazards program in Menlo Park, CA, and made this, their latest research trip, in September 2008. In the distance, walking across a graben at the foot of the scarp is colleague Francesca R. Cinti, with the National Institute of Geophysics and Volcanology in Rome where she studies active tectonics and paleoseismology. They found evidence of earlier faulting behind this top lip.   — Author's photo

Fig. 26—Even huge earth movement (below) can leave humorously stable remnants. Cabin Creek Campground, just off Highway 287 a short distance below Hebgen Dam, near the western end of the Hebgen fault, was split by the scarp. Note that one large tree survived the ground's subsidence upright. A camp trash can clings to the very lip of the scarp, extreme upper right. This photograph was by an Ennis, Montana, commercial photographer, the late Lloyd Skinner. He toured the area soon after the quake and created a series of images for sale as postcards.   — Skinner photo

Fig. 27—Red Canyon fault scarp as it appeared soon after the 1959 earthquake, the same scarp face — plus 49 years of weathering — shown in Fig. 24. From this point the scarp crosses Red Canyon Creek, to the right, and follows the curve of the east valley wall, Fig. 28, before again descending to the level of the old Blarneystone Ranch, Fig. 19.

— Epstein-USGS photo

Fig. 28—A slickenside is the very descriptive geologic term for a surface produced by one earth body slipping past another. Such a surface is often striated in the direction of movement, as this one being inspected by Jack Epstein, standing on the downthrown block. This Red Canyon fault scarp was found on the east east valley wall of Red Canyon Creek.

— Witkind-USGS photo

60

Mudflow

Fig. 29—This mudflow responded to increased subirrigation of the earth below it. Jack Epstein described the eery sensation of standing on the slow-moving mass, hearing and watching trees slowly bend over as the earth altered their root systems. This flow had evidence of prior movement but not in historic time. The 1959 event was not preceded by unusual rainfall, therefore probably was stimulated by the quake's influence on underground water tables. 　　　　　— Epstein-USGS photo

Fig. 30—"WATER FALLS MADE BY NATURE, CABIN CREEK," was the post card identifier used for this Hebgen fault scarp across Cabin Creek, near the site for the Fig. 26 photo. Pre-quake, this stream bed was virtually level.

— Skinner photo

Fig. 31—Within a week of the quake and after the photo in Fig. 30, Cabin Creek's erosive powers had cut the stream scarp down somewhat and dislodged three rocks, lower right side of the white water.   — Epstein-USGS photo

62

Fig. 32—Forty-nine years later, September 2008, the Cabin Creek scarp had disappeared due to the stream's erosive action. Dry-land remnants—the slope across the stream covered by orange leaves, and the bank at the extreme right—remain for the trained eye to identify. David Schwartz makes a point to Suzanne Hacker and Francesca Cinti. Joining the USGS field trip briefly were Dr. Rebecca Bendick of the University of Montana's geological sciences department, and her graduate student, Lewis Kogan, looking toward the scarp, whose research is on development of methods to identify, and estimate the age of, old scarps.   — Author's photo

Rock Creek Campground

Fig. 33—Rock Creek Campground and its spill-over unofficial campsites were either buried under the slide or flooded by Earthquake Lake, shown still filling before construction of a spillway. The Forest Service could provide little information about the campground's location or dimensions. The old, pre-quake highway ran along this timbered slope above the Madison River, through what now is the slide mass and on out the canyon mouth. Notice fallen trees littering the slide surface, indicating its fluid, en masse descent as compared with a tumbling process.

— Epstein-USGS photo

Fig. 34—Before the earthquake and rockslide, the Madison River Canyon looked like this near Rock Creek in an undated photo highlighting the river's fishing reputation. Notice the ridge line, similar to that in Fig. 33. Notice also how the rising water and slide mass diminish the ridge line's apparent height above the canyon bottom.

— Forest Service photo

Fig. 35—Approaching the Madison Canyon slide from the east, one's thoughts range from "beautiful" to "horrible" — from aesthetics of the present to reality of past history. Add to the present slide height 190 feet of water depth at this point to get an idea of pre-quake canyon depth and the force required to push tons of rock so far up the opposite side (on right).

—Author's photo

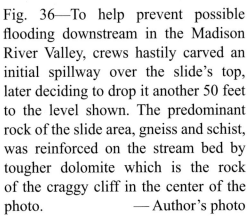

Fig. 36—To help prevent possible flooding downstream in the Madison River Valley, crews hastily carved an initial spillway over the slide's top, later deciding to drop it another 50 feet to the level shown. The predominant rock of the slide area, gneiss and schist, was reinforced on the stream bed by tougher dolomite which is the rock of the craggy cliff in the center of the photo.   — Author's photo

66

Fig. 37—Fragile decomposing rock exposed along the spillway lies in splitting layers such as that found to the top of the slide ridge. One of the predominant rocks in this formation is schist, a word derived from the Greek word meaning "to split." Individual grains easily split off into flakes or slabs. Gneiss (pronounced nais), from the German word gneist (to spark), also is layered, or foliated, and splits off in layers. The USGS geological map of this area estimates age of these rocks as 2.5 billion years.

— Author's photo

Fig. 38—Downstream from the Madison Canyon slide its impressive scar towers over the river, now approximating the pre-quake level. The Bennett family camped somewhere near here under the stars the night of Aug. 17, 1959. These stream banks have been altered since the slide, by heavy equipment and natural erosion.

— Author's photo

Fig. 39—Top-down view of the Madison Canyon rockslide and the mountain ridge from which it flowed. Crescent-shaped indentations along the ridge marking the 1959 slide suggest they repeat an earlier, but much smaller pre-historic slide, now appearing as a treed crescent just beyond (upper right corner). Sharp-edged lines in the center near the spillway are from earth-moving equipment used in spillway construction.
— Chapman photo

68

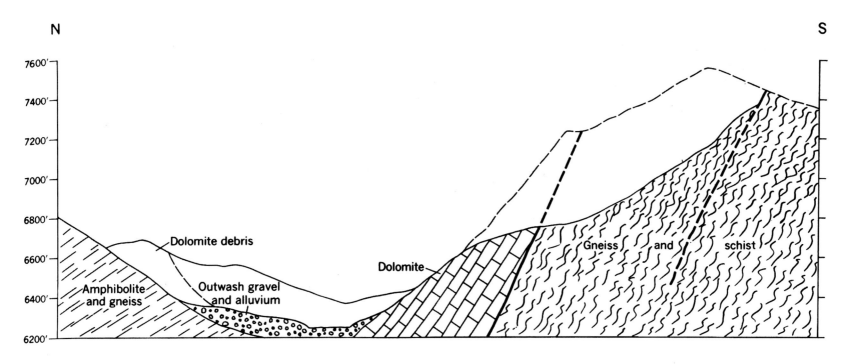

Fig. 40—Cross section of the Madison Canyon at Rock Creek shows how weathered gneiss and schist collapsed off the mountain ridge on the right into the canyon and up its north side. Dolomite had formed a buttress holding the mass of rock in its place, until the earthquake fractured it. An estimated 37 million cubic yards, or 80 million tons, dropped into the canyon and dammed the Madison River. Geologists figured the slide took 20 seconds, start to finish, traveling at approximately 100 miles an hour.

— Illustration from Jarvis B. Hadley's paper in USGS Professional Paper 435

69

Fig. 41—People who say an earthquake makes the earth "shake like jelly" are not kidding. Geologist Irving Witkind and his Weimaraner Tawny scout the demolished Highway 287, located between Hebgen Lake's northern shore, to the left, and the Hebgen fault scarp, upslope. Damage may partially reflect compaction differences in fill material used in construction of the highway. Blacktop thickness seems rather thin by current standards.

— Epstein-USGS photo

Fig. 42—This hillside and highway collapse is not a fault scarp, but it occurred near the deepest known subsidence of the Hebgen fault, 22 feet, further up the hillside. The house, owned by Grace Miller, was located between the highway and Hebgen Lake, where she operated Hillgard Fishing Lodge. After being awakened by the quake, Mrs. Miller, in her 70s, kicked open a jammed door and jumped over a broad crevice bordering her home just before the house and its footings slumped into the lake behind her.

— Epstein-USGS photo

Fig. 43—Hebgen Dam's spillway split away from the concrete core (Fig.44) and had to be replaced. The dam's resident maintenance man estimated water sloshing in the lake after the quake topped the dam by as much as 4 feet. The Hebgen fault scarp parallels this lake shore, about 1,000 feet up the slope behind this maintenance shed. Montana Power Co. built the dam in 1915 to store water for its hydroelectric generating plants downstream.

— Epstein-USGS photo

Fig. 44—Hebgen Dam's concrete core fractured in several places, some cracks up to 6 inches wide. This one also shows some horizontal offset. Earth fill on each side of the core slumped downward and away from the concrete. Another threat to the dam was the seiche action, slow, rolling surges of lake water responding to earth movement. Surges over the dam contributed to soil erosion weakening the fill. Hebgen Dam dropped 9.5 feet in the quake.

— Epstein-USGS photo

Fig. 45—Hebgen Dam, 44 years old when the largest earthquake ever recorded in the Rocky Mountains struck, survived and still stands. Enduring numerous aftershocks through the night, many campers in the canyon below spent anxious hours in fear the dam might fail. Its survival may be thanks to its footing on and abutment into a massive dolomitic rock formation at this penstock end. The formation extends on southwestward through the Henry's Lake Mountains. The dam's northeast end rests in colluvium, relatively loose soil.

— Author's photo

Fig 47—A log cabin, not at Campfire, fared better than its rock chimney when the 7.5 quake hit. Several log cabins at Halford's Resort, downstream from Campfire, were lifted off foundations when Earthquake Lake filled and flooded much of the canyon. They drifted wherever wind blew them, finally settling upstream when lowering the slide spillway dropped the lake level. They now rest in "Ghost Village."

— Epstein-USGS photo

Fig. 46—Wendy and Jim Slatery started operating Campfire Lodge Resort in the spring of 2008. The restaurant, cabins and tent sites sit on the river about a mile below Hebgen Dam. The Slaterys don't fear the dam going out, feeling protected by a cross high on a rocky cliff across the highway that was noticed for the first time, folks told them, the morning after the 1959 Hebgen quake. They went to Campfire for the fishing, fell in love with it because they felt they'd been there before, and bought it when it went up for sale. Earthquake Lake and the slide are downstream.

— Author's photo

Fig. 48—Madison Canyon Rockslide and Earthquake Lake (covered by clouds) occupy the upper right corner of this satellite photograph of Madison Range fault, which crosses the center of the scene, left to right. The Madison fault and scarp somehow escaped significant displacement during the Hebgen event. Madison scarp is a thin, curving line following the base of the Madison Range, left of the highway, and continuing along the Henry's Lake Mountains, to the right. From the north (left), identifiable traces on the ground end at "A," possibly resume by the river at "B" dotted line and definitely pick up again at "B" solid line. It's visible for much of its 40-mile length from highways that parallel both mountain ranges. Geologist Schwartz said Madison's time had not come when the Hebgen quake hit.

— USGS photo by Google Earth photo

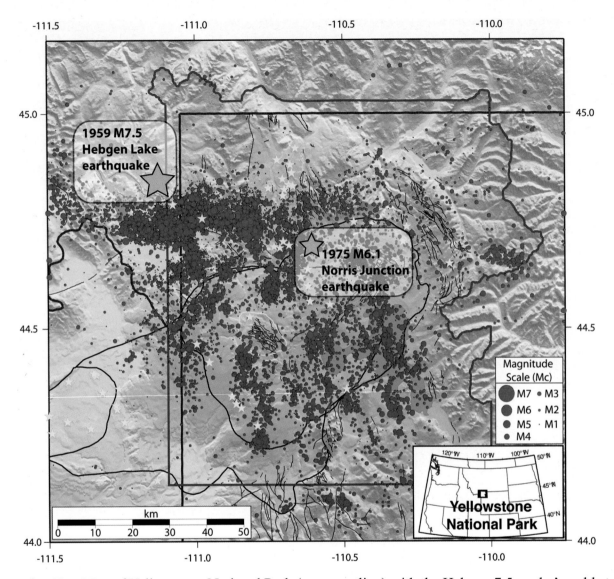

Fig. 49—Map of Yellowstone National Park (green outline) with the Hebgen 7.5 quake's gold star in upper left quadrant. The dense swarm of moderate to large quakes occurred from 1973 to 2002, primarily between the northern side of the Yellowstone caldera and Hebgen Lake. Fault lines in the map include clusters near the center signifying the inflation and deflation of the earth's crust on resurgent domes, Mallard (near Old Faithful) and Sour Creek (north of Yellowstone Lake).— USGS map from Yellowstone Volcano Observatory data, updated by University of Utah Seismographic Stations

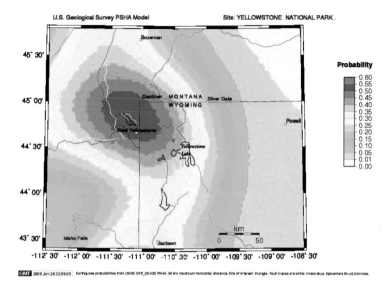

U.S. Geological Survey PSHA Model   Site: YELLOWSTONE NATIONAL PARK.

Fig.50—Probability of an earthquake greater than 5.0 magnitude within 10 years, according to the USGS's online earthquake hazards program, is highest in the Hebgen area and the northwestern corner of Yellowstone National Park. The estimate was dated January 2009. The high probability from calculated rock stress includes the long Madison Range fault and the much shorter Hebgen and Red Canyon faults (all white lines).

— USGS image

Fig. 51—Wood-rail fence near the eastern end of Hebgen Lake exhibits compression stress resulting from the Hebgen quake. Earth within the fence's curvy path compacted, in the direction of arrows. Similar but much more massive compression systems uplifted mountains in the distance. A myriad of underground geological forces such as this are factors in the stress and probability indicated in Fig. 50.

— John R. Stacy-USGS photo

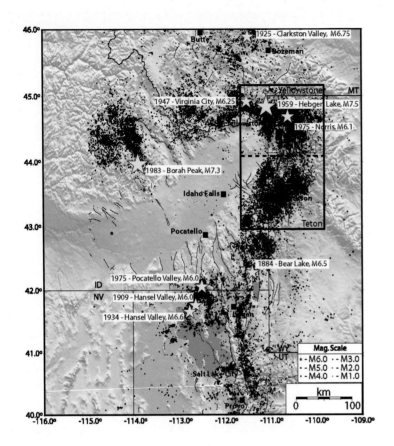

Fig. 52—Part of the Rocky Mountains seismic belt — from Salt Lake City to Butte, Montana, is mapped with major quakes starred and other epicenters marked by dots of varied sizes. The upper square encloses the Hebgen area and part of Yellowstone National Park. The lower square, below dotted line, represents the Teton area.

— USGS map

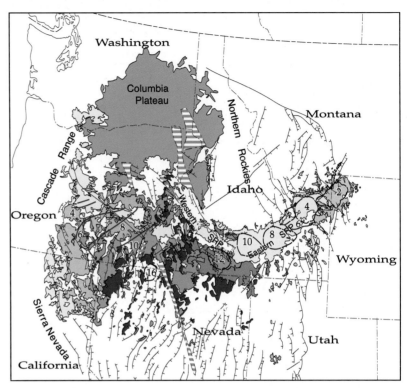

Fig. 53—Map of northwestern United States showing major tectonic and volcanic features covering the last 17 million years. Rhyolites (from explosive eruptions) are shown in shades of red. Basalts (usually slow-moving, highly viscous molten rock flows), are shown in various shades of blue. SRP signifies the Snake River Plain and its chain of volcanic caldera progressing northeastward to Yellowstone country at the conjunction of Wyoming, Montana, and Idaho. Within the past 2 million years, three super volcanoes producing calderas, or collapsed craters, re-shaped the land in what is now Yellowstone National Park (the pink area in Wyoming).

— USGS map after Christiansen and others

Fig. 54—All volcanic eruptions move earth materials from deep underground to build up the surface. Explosive rhyolitic eruptions spew ash and rock fragments thousands of feet into the air, the larger fragments falling near the source, the finer ash windborne for thousands of miles, perhaps around the earth. When hot enough upon landing, usually near the source, particles can fuse together forming rhyolitic welded tuff, such as these pillowy deposits above the Gibbon River, near the northern Yellowstone caldera boundary. The inset shows a close-up of the granules.   — Author's photos

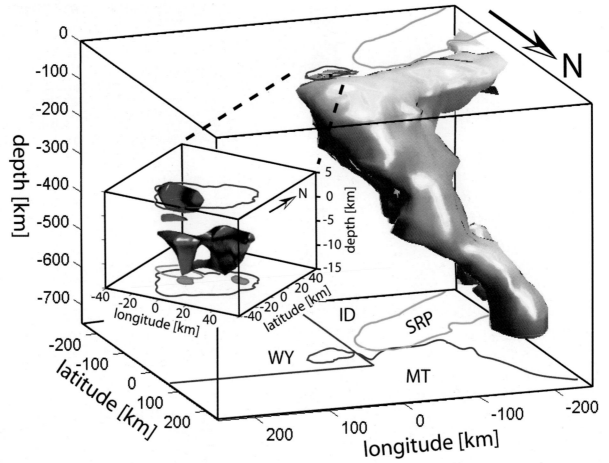

Fig. 55—The Yellowstone "hot spot" and "plume" theories constitute the majority opinion on the region's volcanic past and present, but not without controversy. This image, by Robert B. Smith and colleagues, was made by seismic tomography, for hot rocks the same principle of measuring the return of electronic signals used by a radiologist to make a picture of your liver for diagnosis. This yellow plume's top, about 18 miles below the caldera, is in the center of Yellowstone National Park. Strongest signals from its stem go as deep as 150 miles, with weaker signal returns down to 390 miles, near the mantle transition zone. The stem descends at a 60-degree angle for about 60 surface miles, west northwest toward Dillon, Montana. An upper arm of the plume descends at a shallower angle southeast under the eastern Snake River Plain (SRP). The diagram includes a smaller three-dimensional rendering showing a flat, smaller magma body, perhaps within 6 miles of the caldera surface, separated from the plume top by about 36 miles and probably the most direct source of heat fueling Yellowstone's vast hydrothermal system, the largest concentration on Earth.

— Image by Smith and others

THIS MONOLITH IS A PART OF THE HUGE SLIDE
CAUSED BY THE EARTHQUAKE OF AUGUST 17, 1959.
IT IS DEDICATED TO THE MEMORY OF THE MEN,
WOMEN AND CHILDREN WHOSE LIVES WERE
LOST AS A RESULT OF THE EARTHQUAKE.

IN MEMORIAM

SYDNEY D. A. BALLARD
MARGARET BALLARD
CHRISTOPHER THOMAS BALLARD
PURLEY R. BENNETT
TOM O. BENNETT
CAROLE BENNETT
SUSAN BENNETT
BERNIE L. BOYNTON
INEZ DENDA BOYNTON
MERLE M. EDGERTON, M.D.
EDNA MAE EDGERTON
MARGARET DUFFEY HOLMES
MYRTLE L. PAINTER
ROGER C. PROVOST

ELIZABETH FINDLAY PROVOST
RICHARD PROVOST
DAVID PROVOST
THOMAS MARK STOWE
MARILYN WHITMORE STOWE
EDGAR H. STRYKER
ETHEL M. STRYKER
ROBERT JAMES WILLIAMS
EDITH COY WILLIAMS
STEVEN RUSSELL WILLIAMS
MICHEAL JAMES WILLIAMS
CHRISTY LYN WILLIAMS
HARMON WOODS
EDNA MAUDE WOODS

ERECTED BY
U. S. DEPARTMENT OF AGRICULTURE—FOREST SERVICE

Fig. 56—The Forest Service erected this bronze plaque commemorating the 28 lives lost in the 1959 Hebgen Lake earthquake and rockslide. It is mounted on the largest boulder known to have been transported from one side of the canyon to the other. Rock Creek Campground was instantly buried by rock debris as much as 230 feet deep, covering 130 acres. The memorial overlooks the Earthquake Lake Visitor Center. See Appendix. — Author's photo

Chapter 10

Earth-Building

What has happened here?

My question — and presumably yours, too — refers not only to understanding what happened in present time, but to piece together some antecedents. We will look at recent history, beginning with the 1959 earthquake, and eventually go back past the conventional measure of time. Examining just one segment of geologic history does not adequately tell the story.

Several years ago, flat on my stomach in Montana picking sedimentary rock matrix away from a dinosaur's fossilized appendage, perhaps a humerus, I was overwhelmed by the realization of being practically arm in arm with the remnant of a once-living creature that had not moved for perhaps 70 million years. This layer of fossils lies exposed on the south slope of a hill composed of sedimentary rock and the residue of glacial grinding. The hill above may conceal still more paleontological treasures. The eroded slopes below may already have seen their pieces of biological history ground into common sand and gravel and carried away — bulldozed in large chunks by glaciers or washed in smaller pieces by running water. A level gaze across the expanse of territory falling away to the south makes one wonder if a greater portion of this history is gone than remains, or vice versa. What undiscovered creatures remain anonymous?

Perspective on time makes a difference.

Our geologic story is about dynamic change, never about silent stones and soil merely lying around piled up on Earth's crust. We search tracings of almost indescribable energy bursts — trajectories arcing from the beginning up to contemporary times — and their occasional, fleeting interface with biology, human and otherwise.

In your mind see particles fly-swirl-interact-collide-splinter-combine-float-dissolve-settle-layer-support-sustain-compress-heat-metamorphose-uplift-bend-fold-stress-grind-transport-crack-tower-fall-reproduce-decompose-nourish-sink-melt into the abyss-then fly fly fly again, and again.

All this is nearly invisible to the uninquisitive or self-righteous eye.

Likewise, were it not for the massive Madison River Canyon landslide and our knowledge of the vacationing campers buried there, its triggering earthquake would be, to most of us, a rather unremarkable entry in geologic history. At 7.5 on the Richter scale it was one of the two dozen largest quakes ever recorded in the United States and the largest in recorded history for the Rocky Mountain region. But other than numbers on a page, it leaves for most of us very few discernible clues to its magnitude. Except for the landslide — and even that could be traversed by the unsuspecting motorist as just another ascending or descending grade of the Mountain West — a non-geologist could drive or hike through the area and never detect the different and even larger displacement of the earth's crust that happened simultaneously with the earthquake.

Earth movement on that night fifty years ago was massive.

But it may take human interaction, sometimes tragically, to grab our attention and demand inquiry into nature's past and potential phenomena that exist hidden right under our noses.

"You, you, you. . .and you go"

Strength of the quake created a sense of urgency within the U. S. Geological Survey. So before noon the morning after the quake, at USGS headquarters in Denver, the supervisor, knowing Witkind and Epstein already were there, gathered his staff and said, "You, you, you. . .and you go."

Warren Hamilton remembers it well. He was one of them: "The assumption was that money to pay for it would come from somewhere." A half-dozen men, followed later by others, were on their way to West Yellowstone, Montana, early the next day.

Each man was more or less autonomous and could make choices about where to concentrate his efforts, says Hamilton, who paired with W. Bradley Myers to focus on the young geology of the West Yellowstone basin and the very young volcanic rocks to its south.

While others concentrated on understanding faulting in the old rocks, "Brad and I saw immediately that this story had to be in the newer materials, not the old ones," says Hamilton as I interview him at the suggestion of his old adversary, Irving Witkind. "And so we thought that they wasted much of their time." His voice trailed off.

Territorial imperative was still alive, nearly 50 years later.

As it turned out, Witkind and his colleagues chose specific, single topics for their surveys, while Hamilton-Myers made a comprehensive report on the whole area, integrating topics and localities others had studied.

Thinking broadly may be Hamilton's trademark.

He calls me over to a high table surface where he can lay out maps and work — still, after more than 13 years of retirement — while standing. This is a satellite map showing topographic relief for much of the western United States. He's already talked about the San Andreas fault in California, which comes up just west of San Francisco and represents the slipping of the Pacific Ocean floor relative to North America. Prior to 30 million years ago its movement was subduction, one plate diving beneath another. But since then it's been strike-slip, where one or both sides of a fault line move horizontally against one another. One moment Hamilton is explaining how earthquakes and/or continental plate movements on one side of the map could affect the rock architecture of the West Yellowstone basin over on the other side of the map, more than a thousand miles away.

During this time, he says, the Pacific "is drifting obliquely away and North America is keeping up by stretching or extending back here" — as he points to caterpillar-like squiggles on the topographic map denoting mountain ranges between the Sierra Nevada and the Colorado Plateau. "The ranges are sliding into the valleys.

"A direction change is not all that startling given all the movement," Hamilton says. "The movement is still going on. The earth is in motion. A major problem is to see through or past the fault scarp immediately before you to envision movement on a regional basis."

But we do need to see that rock surface before us. What geologists accomplished after the Hebgen quake had never been done before, Hamilton says. And that was to possess before and after elevations from highway survey profiles and benchmarks in a line paralleling a fault scarp, the Hebgen, making it possible to measure absolute ground subsidence or uplift, and not just relative motion. It is a profile of the earth's movement. Myers and Hamilton measured the changes in the

Hebgen Lake shoreline, tied these to the highway profiles, and thus extended the absolute elevation changes over a larger area.

Fault-induced earth movement had been measured before, of course, by triangulation and trilateration. Before and after positions were known for the Hayward quake in 1868 and the 1906 San Francisco quake resulting from the San Andreas fault. It was the latter which gave Henry Fielding Reid the data from which he developed the elastic rebound theory, says David P. Schwartz of the USGS' Earthquake Hazard Project. This was the first satisfactory understanding of how earthquakes occur as the result of faults. As rocks bend under strain they store increasing energy, until a fracture (fault) suddenly releases the energy. The rocks then rebound back to their original shape, but the opposing sides of the fault have moved relative to one another.

A Huge Quake, One of Many

An area of some 175 square miles — perhaps more — stretching northwest from the west side of Yellowstone National Park, fell virtually as a unified block by as much as 22 feet. Dropped, or as geologists say, it subsided. Maybe not in one bang but possibly ratcheting down in a rapid series of jerks.

In fact, one man described his bed repeatedly falling out from under him — like bump, bump, bump. His cabin was close to the fault scarp's greatest displacement, along the northern edge of the falling Hebgen block. The least displacement was at the southeastern corner of the block, near West Yellowstone, Montana, but also along the southern side and at its western extremity. These least affected sections were almost like a hinge as the fault block — constituting much of the broad West

Yellowstone Basin — fell, warped somewhat, and tilted toward the northwest.

Included in the fall was Hebgen Lake, more than 17 miles long and 6 miles across at its widest. The subsidence and tilt changed the lake's shoreline and enlarged its storage capacity but, otherwise, did no damage to the reservoir.

A "fault" is the fracture in bedrock along which rocks on both sides have moved, usually buried far below the surface. The "fault scarp" is the visible sheared face, often in loose surface material — topsoil, sand and gravel — defining the surface expression of the subsurface fault. Red Canyon and Hebgen faults apparently are part of a complex system, one splitting from the other (Fig. 25), according to Dr. Diane I. Doser, professor geological sciences at the University of Texas at El Paso.

She visualizes faulting as tearing a piece of bread from a loaf: "The torn surface will be uneven because patches of bread will be stronger or weaker in various places. One of these rough patches breaks and then the rupture travels along the fault to break the next patch. Eventually the rupture hits a very strong rough spot and stops."

Further evidence of the Hebgen-Red Canyon complexity cited by Doser is the 5- to 8-second delay (computed from seismic analyses) between an initial shock and the larger second jolt, and that the two actually may have come from two distinct events. "It could have started on one small patch of the fault and then picked up speed and got larger as the rupture progressed along the fault," she wrote for the Journal of Geophysical Research. "This is not unusual for earthquakes above magnitude 7."

It is difficult to say how deep or thick this block is, or what subterranean structure(s) it now rests upon. Estimates of the seismic depth of the initial fault rupture range from 6 to 7.5 miles. The maximum depth of aftershocks was about 10 miles.

There are different descriptions of what might have caused the fracture, but there is no disputing the fact that new fault scarps joined traces of old ones whose origins go back millions of years. This massive Hebgen block has fallen repeatedly but only once in recorded history, 1959. The fault trend lines show a general northwest-southeast orientation, originating in the northwest corner of Yellowstone and extending along the northerly trend of the Madison Range as it abuts the western edge of the Gallatin Range. Maps depicting the dozens of earthquake epicenters as dots appear in the shape of an arrowhead pointing northwest out of the northwest corner of the park, pointing a line similar to that of the faulting.

This Yellowstone region is second in the contiguous 48 states only to the San Andreas fault areas of California for earthquake, or seismic, activity.

For Yellowstone, heat alone is sufficient to produce uplifts and deflation of the earth's crust, movements that produce faults and earthquakes. But added to that dynamic are the tectonic earth movements and faults that are products of shifting earth crustal systems much larger and far beyond Yellowstone's rare heat supply.

Although there may be no direct connection, the area of these quakes loosely defines the upper Madison River watershed, which drains much of the western half of the park. The Gibbon River, which drains the Norris Geyser Basin, and the Firehole River, which drains Old Faithful and the Upper and Lower Geyser basins, join at Madison Junction to form

the Madison River which flows northwesterly, exiting the park about 4 miles north of West Yellowstone.

With their headwaters both rising in the western part of the park, the Madison River flowing northwest and the Gallatin River going north, both streams eventually join — some 100 miles north — with the Jefferson River to form the Missouri River at Three Forks, Montana, west of Bozeman.

The West Yellowstone basin, broad and relatively flat (Fig. 2), is the top of the Hebgen fault block that dropped as much as 22 feet, an average of 10 feet, during the quake. As a major water collector for the Madison, it is no wonder the former Montana Power Company, now NorthWestern Energy, chose this basin as the site of its Hebgen Dam, which formed Hebgen Lake in 1915 as a water storage reservoir for the utility's hydroelectric dams downstream. And as a catchment area, much of the basin's surface also is covered with the outflow of volcanic eruptions, rhyolite lava, and/or obsidian sand and gravel, also of volcanic origin — all of it either falling out from one of Yellowstone's explosive eruptions or ground up and transported there by glacial or stream action.

Repeated faulting and subsiding created this basin with its drain point where the Gallatin and Madison mountain ranges and the Henry's Lake Mountains jam together.

The West Yellowstone Basin

Standing at the West Yellowstone airport, just outside of town, look northwest, across Hebgen Lake (Fig. 2). I visualize a baseball park: I'm standing at home plate; the right field foul line extends to the north, toward Bozeman, Montana; as the right field stands rise up from the outfield, they become the Gallatin Range; beyond deep center field rises the Madison Range; beyond left field are the Henry's Lake Mountains and the foul line drops over a low pass into Idaho; second base is near the middle of Hebgen Lake. This analogy cannot be used literally but it gives a sense of place, of the flat basin relative to the rising mountains surrounding much of it. Yellowstone National Park is behind. At the far end of the lake is Hebgen Dam, not center-field distance, but 17 miles away

The Madison River flows westward out of the park, around our right shoulder. It soon becomes the Madison Arm of Hebgen Lake.

The Red Canyon fault scarp starts up to our right, in low-lying hills near where the quake epicenter was first thought to be. The fault cracks westward before curving right and side-winding up the mountain along Red Canyon Creek, then crossing the creek and climbing high toward the west to parallel the broad curve of Kirkwood Ridge (Fig. 23) before plunging down again.

Starting near Red Canyon's sharp turn up to the north, the Hebgen fault scarp strikes its northwestward path — as if one of the faults splits away from the other where Red Canyon makes its sudden change of direction. (See the map on inside front cover.)

Instead of Red Canyon's circuitous route up and around the Kirkwood slope, the Hebgen scarp follows a comparatively straight route not far above Hebgen Lake's northern shoreline. In addition to the lake shore, the scarp parallels Highway 287. It lies on the relatively flat basin floor rather than climbing up the mountainside.

The Red Canyon scarp covers about 14 miles on the ground, the Hebgen about 8. Both faults are old and fractured again and again in pre-historic times, but only once, in 1959, in recorded history.

The West Yellowstone Basin virtually is the top of the Hebgen fault block of nearly 150 square miles. Red Canyon block of some 25 square miles mostly slants up the mountainside to Kirkwood Ridge. Apparently, the two blocks subsided in tandem.

As you look up the timbered mountainside to find the Red Canyon fault scarp, the most pronounced rock face you will see is the Kirkwood Ridge, not Red Canyon scarp (Fig. 23). The latter appears from a distance to be a ledge cut into the mountain for a logging road. The two scars are roughly parallel. Kirkwood Ridge is evidence of the thrust faulting that created these mountains during the Laramide Orogeny, between 70 and 40 million years ago. Instead of the normal faulting now being seen in Hebgen and Red Canyon structures — one side dropping relative to the other side of the fracture — Kirkwood Ridge resulted from rock strata being thrust upward, past vertical, until folding back and breaking apart, leaving the massive limestone face we call Kirkwood. In addition to her own field work, Doser cited earlier work by Witkind and Myers for her 1985 paper *Source Parameters and Faulting Processes of the 1959 Hebgen Lake Earthquake,* published in the Journal of Geophysical Research.

Remarkably, the age difference of these two similar and parallel rock scars — Red Canyon and Kirkwood — is many millions of years. Red Canyon is a true fault scarp which appeared in 1959. Kirkwood is a resistant rock layer exposed for several miles by erosion over the millennia. The two features may, however, have common roots.

Beyond Kirkwood Ridge, the Gallatin Range stretches some 60 miles northward toward Bozeman. Further to the west a higher mountain range, the Madison, extends northward. Almost as an extension southward of the Madison Range, the

Henry's Fork Mountains complete the elevated ring around much of the West Yellowstone Basin.

Picture 17-mile-long Hebgen Lake ending near where the Hebgen fault scarp ends. That's also the location of Hebgen Dam. Here the topography changes radically. Below the dam, the Madison River again briefly flows freely through the Madison Canyon but soon becomes impounded again, as Earthquake Lake. It is here, the river veers away from its northwesterly trend, turning toward the southwest to cut through a mountain barrier.

The Cataclysmic Slide

Cataclysm = Any violent change involving sudden and extensive alteration of the earth's surface.

It all happened in about 20 seconds.

After millions of geologic seasons of canyon-carving, earth-shaping natural events, the Madison River had become a trout-fishing paradise — six miles of smooth tongues of current flowing between sparkling riffles, boulders steadfastly guarding the fish resting places offered by "keeper holes," and a water chemistry sustaining numerous hatches of various wiggling and flying nutrients.

As hungry trout discover where to find insect concentrations, so do fishers learn where to find trout. They gather in places like this. Two commercial resorts with cabins. Two Forest Service campgrounds, one called Rock Creek, near the far end of the canyon where the river makes a sudden bend before emptying into the broad valley. At the bend, earth's forces left a big rock

wall and created a long, leisurely pool. It's no wonder that fishers camped near it.

Somewhere above, this south wall of the canyon split apart from the quake's shaking and filled the canyon bottom — crushing the campground and some of its occupants, throwing other campers into deadly chaos and damming the Madison River.

Thus Earthquake Lake.

A buttress of strong dolomitic rock outcroppings lies in what appears from a distance as a horizontal layer, about half-way up from the old river level to the ridge top. Up close, one can see this dolomite's strata are nearly vertical, the formation having been laid over on its side ages before, as explained more fully later. This buttress gave way with the quake and allowed the collapse, from above and behind it, of the slide mass: 80 million tons of weaker gneiss and schist rock of a flaky, splitting nature and whose weathered strata were angled sharply downward, primed to slide into the river given any opportunity.

One geologist stated that this mass of rock traveled at possibly 100 miles an hour down across the river and 430 feet up the north canyon wall.

Nineteen campers are thought to be buried under fractured rock. The mound measured three-fourths of a mile long, a mile wide and 230 feet deep. This debris covered approximately 130 acres. Evidence at the upstream edge of the slide indicates that a wave of muddy water carrying trees, driftwood, and small rocks was pushed ahead of the slide mass, reaching above the river on the north canyon wall. This air blast and wave fractured trees and caused death, serious injury, and panic among campers, and extensive property damage and loss of personal gear.

On the slide's downstream edge, a similar wave struck two family campsites, carried logs up to three-fourths of a mile downstream and rolled two battered automobiles 100 yards below the slide. It is difficult to understand how two people, Irene Bennett and her son Phil, could have survived such trauma.

The Madison slide is by far the most visible landmark of the Hebgen earthquake and is one of the largest U. S. landslides ever recorded. Its volume of about 37 million cubic yards of material is nearly the same as the 1903 Turtle Mountain slide at Frank, Alberta, just north of the border with Canada, and about three-fourths the size of the 1925 Gros Ventre slide in northwestern Wyoming, near Grand Teton National Park. Turtle Mountain killed 76 persons and buried most of a small coal-mining town in the canyon. The Gros Ventre was not near habitation and claimed no lives at the time, although its natural dam of the Gros Ventre River gave out due to a wet spring two years later, releasing a flood that drowned six persons and destroyed the homes and barns of 80 residents four miles downstream.

In Madison Canyon, the quake broke the dolomite buttress and suddenly changed the rock pile's friction quotient that largely had held the unstable mountainside in place.

Geologist Jarvis B. Hadley of the U. S. Geological Survey wrote: ".... A mass of weak rock, held in place largely by friction, was suddenly transformed into a mass which literally flowed into the canyon. Also important is the evidence that this fluidity was produced simultaneously over the slide area. Factors tending to reduce the internal friction or resistance to sliding, or to overcome this resistance by imparting momentum to the mass, are presumably responsible for the sudden change from solid to fluid behavior. Water content did not cause it for there had been no rain for six weeks."

Only the earthquake can be blamed. Hadley pointed out that a sudden subsidence in the slide area would have produced a momentary decrease in the gravitational force holding back the slide mass — like a roller coaster ride which lifts you off your seat as it plunges down just after peaking — "and would have been most effective in reducing the frictional resistance" to sliding.

Rock Creek Campground

The U. S. Forest Service could produce no records of when Rock Creek Campground was established. But it likely started as a favorite fishing location, with campers adding fire rings and parking spaces until eventual official campground designation by the Forest Service years later. It was located near a small seasonal stream of the same name, on the north side of the Madison River. Rock Creek is the last stream feeding the river before the canyon spills out onto the flat, broad Madison Valley.

The campground had five official sites, with picnic tables and fire pits, and these were located just upstream from the slide edge. Because of the crowd, campers settled for locations not officially designated and many of these people were buried. One camper said he counted 21 trailers that day between the mouth of the canyon and where he finally parked. This estimate could include sites either above or below the slide, as well as those buried by slide debris.

Other would-be campers, finding no room, passed by and only later learned of the disaster they somehow missed.

Survivors who camped at the edge of the slide — and some who did not survive — were literally tumbled from their tents or camp trailers by the sudden blast of air and river water displaced by the collapsing mountain. Some of these people do not differentiate between first hearing the quake's rumbling and then the roar of the mountain falling. It's a blur. Others have widely varying estimates of passing time. The panic and hysteria — and inability to report with total consistancy — are no surprise. A witness who was about four and a half miles up the canyon, closer to the quake epicenter, recalls a gap of "a minute or two" between the initial quake sounds and the thunderous roar of the slide. It's a time lag explained at least in part by distance, in part because he awakened in a cabin which probably started rattling with the very earliest vibrations.

The Tilt

There is solid evidence — a strange, ironic choice of phrase in a description of natural phenomena which defy solidity — that the West Yellowstone basin not only subsided but tilted significantly.

Subsidence was least at West Yellowstone, increasing toward the northwest. Deepest subsidence was about 22 feet, slightly less than a mile from Hebgen Dam. For both the Hebgen and Red Canyon faults, subsidence was greatest near the centers of the scarps, tapering off toward their ends.

Think of four people holding a blanket flat out, tightly, one person at each corner with the blanket's long dimension on a northwest-southeast axis. One corner, on the southeast, is imagined near West Yellowstone. Standing to that person's right is the northeast corner, close to the boundary of Yellowstone National Park. Proceeding counter clockwise around the blanket, we come to the northwest corner, located just beyond Hebgen Dam. And the last corner, on the southwest point, is located on the west side of the Madison Range in the Madison Valley. They hold the corners tight, sloping slightly toward the northwest corner, that is, in the direction of the basin's drainage.

The fault fractures, the quake shakes. The West Yellowstone corner drops hardly at all. The northeast corner, near the quake's epicenter, and the southwest corner, near the huge prehistoric Madison fault line that deformed very little this time, drops

moderately. But the northwest corner of the blanket drops a lot, and the northern edge of the blanket droops down. This side of the blanket is parallel to the Hebgen fault and Highway 287 and somewhat parallel to the looping trend of the Red Canyon fault.

This tilting repeats similar prehistoric geologic shifts that make the Madison drainage/West Yellowstone basin what it is, a northwest-flowing system. Once upon a time, this drainage from the Yellowstone region flowed differently.

Aside from the Madison slide, this northward tilt of Hebgen Lake was the most dramatic evidence of the earthquake and Hebgen block subsidence. The south shoreline was exposed as water shifted north. On the north shore, a landslide slumped a large area into the lake, relocating the north shore further north (Fig. 42). One section of highway nearly a half mile long was submerged, the asphalt on either end disappearing into a newly formed bay of the relocated lake. Summer cabins along the shore were flooded and demolished.

The Seiche

Destruction of lakeshore cabins was caused in part by the sloshing action on the lake — technically called a "seiche" — following the sudden subsidence. Different from a tidal wave or tsunami, motion of a seiche is similar to the slow roll of water in a flat pan as it accidentally tilts in your grasp. The water rises to the left, possibly splashing over the edge, then retreats back to the right end of the pan, repeating in decreasing volume.

People at Hebgen Dam told of seeing the seiche roll to and fro. "Whoever heard of a lake that literally disappears?" Witkind asked. "Standing at the dam you could look down and see the lake floor, and then the water comes back, kind of slowly."

By the time dam attendants George Hungerford and Lester Caraway reached the dam that night, they estimated the peak swell topped the structure by approximately 4 feet. It was not a quick wave soon gone, but a rise of the lake level that persisted for a few minutes. Water gradually lowered, according to the U. S. Geological Survey report, "to the point where much of the upstream face of the dam was exposed."

The swell retreated southeast to the upper end of the lake before returning at a lower height an estimated 17 minutes later, although this frequency has always been in dispute. Because of general confusion and near panicked concern about integrity of the then 44-year-old earth-filled concrete-cored dam structure, Hungerford and Caraway could only estimate water heights and time spans. But they watched the seiche top the dam at least three more times before the volume could be handled through the spillway.

Peak discharge over the dam and through the spillway was computed at 14,000 cubic feet per second (cfs).

Hungerford, Caraway and their wives lived in homes below the dam. The alarmed foursome first rushed to a stream gauge located about 1,500 feet downstream from the dam. They had not been at the gauge more than a minute or two before they reported seeing a five-foot wave of water rolling down the river toward them. This presumably was outwash from the first seiche over the dam but at the time they were not sure what it was.

Assuming the dam was failing, they scrambled about 100 feet up to the road — out of the canyon bottom and away from possible flooding — and hastened to the dam. A road angles up from the river to the northeastern end of the dam, where the canyon suddenly broadens out for the lake and the West Yellowstone basin.

Hungerford remembers arriving there about 11:55 p.m., or 18 minutes after the quake's first shocks. The earthen downstream side of the dam was already wet and somewhat eroded by the first seiche. Earth fill had slumped down from the top, away from the concrete core on both sides and toward the southeastern end of the dam.

Geologist Hamilton calculated that subsidence and tilting at the moment the Hebgen block dropped left water in the lower, main body of the lake 10 to 15 feet lower than water in the lake's upper reaches. This tilting of the lake bottom started sloshing water back and forth, up and down the lake. He believes Hungerford and Caraway, in their excitement, exaggerated the depth of water topping the dam. Hamilton found evidence in vegetation along the shoreline indicating the maximum depth of flow over the dam was 1½ feet rather than 4 feet.

A man who happened to be up and about at the time of the quake, standing on the lake shore near Kirkwood Creek, reported being knocked down by the first jolt. He struggled to his feet to see a 10-foot wave coming northeast toward him, followed by a 15-foot wave traveling northwest, then another small wave approaching him obliquely across the lake.

A man on the southeast part of the lake reported waves coming toward him, followed by the shoreline receding away from him, which caused him to believe the dam must have burst and the lake was draining.

Hebgen Dam Held

In any case, how could the dam have held? First came a large jolt and a drop of nearly 10 feet, then tremendous water pressure from the seiche, serious erosion of its earth-fill support and then continued aftershocks.

The concrete core sustained four cracks up to six inches wide (Figs. 43 and 44), but the whole structure held in spite of a drop of 9.5 feet, as measured at the northeast end. Footings of the southwest end of the dam core (on the left end looking downstream) are integrated into a stratum of dolomite similar to but much larger than that which failed at the slide.

Even more important, the Hebgen fault scarp, as indicated by Witkind's post-quake research paper, passes within approximately 1,000 feet of the northeast abutment of the dam, which rests upon the edge of a large colluvial cone slumping off the north side of the canyon. Colluvium is loose material, sand and gravel, that has been emplaced by gradual gravitational slumping — such as a slow landslide — in contrast to alluvium, which has been deposited usually by running water.

With hindsight influenced by modern construction standards and geological knowledge, it is difficult to comprehend how a dam could knowingly have been designed for construction so close to a fault line, or seated in such loose material. Not known is upon what geological data the dam location and design were based.

Apparently, no one in 1915 knew of the pre-historic subterranean fault, or the possibility of a new fracture which, in this case, came 44 years after construction.

The earliest recorded speculation about a possible Hebgen fault was by J. T. Pardee in 1950, according to Kathy Haller of the USGS Geologic Hazards Team in Denver. In his paper, "Late Cenozoic Block Faulting in Western Montana," published in the Geological Society of America Bulletin, Pardee noted a strong indication of a fault-controlled range front along the northeast side of Hebgen Lake, but he did not cite a fault name. The earliest known use of the fault name was by Witkind, Myers, Hamilton and others post-1959.

(NOTE: Pardee was the USGS geologist whose studies of the Missoula, Montana, area convinced him that a huge glacial lake had once existed there but had suddenly drained —

apparently several times — with failure of the glacier dam on what is now called the Clark Fork River. Meanwhile, J Harlen Bretz, a geology professor at the University of Chicago and later at the University of Washington, refined his theory that the channeled scablands of eastern and central Washington had been scoured out by one or more huge floods. Finally, working contemporaneously but apart, Pardee's source and Bretz's consequence melded into a unfied history of the Glacial Lake Missoula floods and their remarkable re-shaping of the basaltic terrain of the Columbia Basin in Washington.)

Geology is a mysterious science to most folks and opinions change slowly.

Even if the Hebgen fault had been definitely identified at the time of construction, says Schwartz of the USGS, "It wouldn't have made a difference. In 1915 no one worried about that stuff." Schwartz works out of Menlo Park, California, and is a student of earthquake hazards.

"There are many references in the 1920s when a quake was seen as the cause of a fault, rather than vice versa," he says. Thus, in the early 1900s, a prehistoric fault scarp, having not weathered away and still visible, probably would not have been recognized as a potential danger.

Hebgen Dam lies perpendicular to the fault line in an area where subsidence of the Hebgen Lake block suddenly decreased, by as much as half, as measured by the highway survey benchmarks along the north side of the lake and by shoreline changes. Buried bedrock features obviously changed in character in this area and it is fortunate the dam was not built closer to the fault's maximum subsidence of 22 feet just a mile to the southeast.

A supposition by the author: This 90-degree relation of the dam to the fault may have been to the dam's advantage. For if the earthquake represents a stretching of the basin floor away from the fault line and the mountainside beyond it, the dam's axis is parallel to the direction of crustal movement. An angle other than perpendicular to the fault line could have produced shear forces and caused structural twisting making collapse more likely.

Although battered, the dam stands today (Fig. 45).

And geologist Hamilton would say it's all location, location, location.

"I doubt that any consideration was given to earthquake potential at the time (of the dam's construction)," Hamilton said in our 50-year-followup interview. "It was just topographically a good place — a narrow bedrock canyon with a big valley upstream from it." In other words: Construction efficiency in 1915 meant finding a narrow river gap which would require less concrete to span. Combining with this human pragmatism was the serendipitous geology that made the dam's fault-induced downward plunge less than half as deep as the lake's subsidence a mere mile away.

Pacific Power & Light-Montana (PPLM) owns Hebgen Dam, acquiring in 1999 all the hydroelectric generating facilities formerly built and operated by Montana Power Co. Lisa Reid Perry, manager of community affairs for PPLM, says no technical geologic or engineering information going back to the time of construction, 1915, could be found. Federal officials concerned with dam safety could not release such information, they say, even if they had records from that time, because of tightened Homeland Security Act legislation.

"On Aug. 17, 1959, this dam survived one of the most severe earthquake shocks to which a fill dam in the United States has ever been exposed," says a description supplied by the Dam Safety Unit of the Montana Dept. of Natural Resources and Conservation.

Originally there was a small powerhouse at the site, providing power for the dam and nearby campsite operations. These generating units were eliminated in 1966 when a 12.5 kilovolt electric distribution line was extended from Ennis.

The concrete core of the dam is 87 feet high and 712 feet long at its top, tapering down to 573 feet long as the canyon walls taper inward at the base. The structure is 16 feet thick at the base, which is on dolomitic bedrock, and three feet thick at the top. The earth and rock fill is 20 feet wide at the crest, which includes a service road from the northeast end at the highway, extending to the intake control equipment at the opposite end to the southwest. A layer of the gravel and rock fill on either side of the dam core was partially cemented by lime during construction.

A new spillway, replacing the quake-damaged original, is 47 feet wide and angles 677 feet down to the river from the northeastern end of the dam.

Gerald Yetter, 76, a retired rancher now living on the shore of Hebgen Lake, remembers Montana Power Co. crews digging down beside the dam's concrete core to inspect for damage. "They found fractures," Yetter told me. "I saw all the breaks and cracks … They went down whatever a back hoe could reach, 10 feet or so." He was not sure how the breaks were repaired.

Yetter was employed after the quake to send hourly radio dispatches to the downstream town of Ennis to report on the dam's condition. He and others monitored and reported around the clock for two months to say, "The dam's still holding." Such was anxiety at the time.

Of course integrity of the dam caused much more panicky concern the night of the quake for the more than a hundred vacationers temporarily trapped between the dam and the slide. While marveling that the dam apparently had survived the first tremors, aftershocks continued and people feared the worst as they scampered to higher ground. Until dawn, most people in the canyon did not even know of the immense slide which blocked their escape downstream, nor that the tilting Hebgen Lake's disappearing shoreline had flooded the highway and eliminated the other route out to the east. They huddled at the highest level spot they knew of, a spot some regulars to the canyon knew to be slightly higher than lake level.

Another dam-safety scare occurred in September 2008 with the malfunction of two of the four intake gates that control flow of lake water through a penstock and out under Hebgen Dam. For nearly three weeks the Madison River below the dam flowed about four times normal volume for the season and Hebgen Lake dropped quickly to its winter level before they brought the flow under control. Uncertainty about what caused the malfunction prompted the Forest Service to order temporary closure of its campground and a commercial cabin and camping resort a short distance below the dam.

Work crews repaired the intake and restored normal water flow but more modification was planned for later, according to Mark Lambrecht, spokesman for the current dam owner, PPLM. He said sensors, called piezometers, are buried in the dam to detect internal structural movement and/or flow changes. These are checked daily on-site. No abnormal readings were detected during the emergency, Lambrecht said, and he knew of no official opinion whether there was a connection between failure of the intake control gates and a 2.3 earthquake in the area earlier the same day. Quakes of that size are fairly common in the region.

Help from Another Time

Despite being quake-shaken, there were people that night who knew the highest point of the canyon road had an elevation approximately 90 feet higher than the lake's full-pool altitude of 6,544 feet above sea level. As mentioned earlier, survivors headed there and eventually dubbed the high ground Refuge Point.

That safety spot had been created thousands of years before — recent in geologic time — by other earth-building flows into the Madison Canyon from the north, from the large Beaver Creek drainage. Alluvium carried by stream action and glacial till make a major delta-shaped intrusion into the canyon there, forcing the river to flow around the end of it.

Flooding was, in fact, an immediate problem for survivors of the slide, although not because of the feared failure of Hebgen Dam. Normal flow of the Madison River was immediately dammed by the slide and started creating Earthquake Lake, its level rising an average of 9 feet per day. In just over 3 weeks the new lake extended back from the slide/dam nearly 6 miles to the base of Hebgen Dam. A few cars and some camping gear still are at the bottom of the lake's lower end. Also flooded by about three feet of water was Campfire Lodge, a commercial resort not far below the dam.

Authorities feared that river erosion over the top of the slide would de-stabilize the slide and so they cut a shallow spillway. That waterway later was cut down another 50 feet and lined with some of the dolomite rock that had led the slide rampage. (Engineers remembered the flooding and devastation of the Gros Ventre River slide not far away, 34 years before, and so were cautious.) This left a new lake 190 feet deep, four miles long, and a free-flowing Madison River for two miles between the dam and the head of the lake.

Profile of the Subsidence

Highway survey benchmarks closely parallel the Hebgen fault scarp and provide reliable and virtually unique reference points upon which to measure subsidence. The federal Coast and Geodetic Survey ran levels on the Highway 287 route in 1934 and again after the quake, in September and October of 1959. This 25-year period may have produced other subsidence, but most of the drop represented by the following figures is believed to have happened in the earthquake. All subsidences of benchmarks listed below are in feet:

Driving north from West Yellowstone on Highway 191, then northwest on Highway 287:

West Yellowstone	-0.003
Madison Arm bridge	-1.5
Horse Butte Road	-1.9
Duck Creek Junction (turn northwest)	-0.3
Grayling Creek bridge	-10.4
Lakeview Resort	-12.5
Dave Johnson Creek	-18.5
Kirkwood Creek	-21.0
Hilgard Lodge	-22.0
Hebgen Dam	-9.5
Cabin Creek Campground	-8.0
Campfire Lodge	-8.3
Beaver Creek	-7.0
One mile beyond Beaver Creek	-13.0
(Several comparisons missing: terrain flooded by Earthquake Lake or buried by slide.)	
Stagger Ranch	-7.0
Near Highway 87 junction	-3.4
Madison River Lodge	-1.4
Three miles north of Papoose Creek	-0.1

We can see that subsidence started increasing sharply west of Duck Creek Junction. Its maximum known drop, at Hilgard Lodge, was near the northwest end of the lake. Subsidence fortunately decreased sharply from there on and is only -9.5 feet by the time we reach the dam.

It's anyone's guess how much more movement of ground the dam could have sustained. But it appears that the dam and its abutments into the canyon walls all dropped together. The dam's subsidence correlates generally with the new, lower level of the lake.

Continuing downstream from Hebgen Dam, subsidence readings are incomplete as many benchmarks are flooded under Earthquake Lake. At Stagger Ranch, located on the west slope of the Madison Range where the canyon mouth opens into the Madison Valley and the river turns northward toward Ennis, subsidence on the highway was -7.0 feet, but within two miles west was half that at -3.4 and two miles further was halved again at -1.4 feet.

As you drive westward out of the canyon on Highway 287, you pass directly over another major geologic feature which in pre-historic times shaped the region, the Madison Range fault (Fig. 48).

The Madison Range Fault

Stagger Ranch sits astride the fault's scarp and is visible from the highway on the right (to the north) almost immediately as you emerge from the canyon into the Madison Valley. The 1959 quake caused some subsidence along this old scar, but its displacement was minor compared with that experienced by the

Hebgen and Red Canyon scarps. From a distance, the old scarp shows as a long horizontal band of discolored soil running for several miles along the western base of the Madison Range, where the mountain rises sharply from the relatively flat plane of the valley floor.

At the canyon mouth, highway construction and leveling created by the river have hidden or obliterated the scarp until it reappears similarly positioned at the mountain base south of the river.

This long scar is a composite scarp produced by repeated faulting and earthquakes during the past 15,000 years, plus or minus, not by some recent event, according to Schwartz. Geologists Clyde P. Ross and Willis H. Nelson wrote in *Professional Paper 435* that relative displacement along the fault scarp has totaled several thousand feet over the ages. The displacement it shows currently ranges from 10 to 30 feet.

The scarp was known well before 1959. In 1926 geologist Pardee determined that the most recent movement along the scarp had been sometime prior to 1770. He based his estimate on dating the stump of an old tree found near the top of the scarp, representing the minimum age of the scarp rather than the date of a quake. Ross and Nelson estimated that an earthquake which produced such a scarp — judging by its 40-mile length as well as its vertical displacement — could possibly have been more powerful than the Hebgen. More about this important fault later.

Technically, mountains south of the Madison Canyon and extending to Henry's Lake, over Raynolds Pass, are designated as the Henry's Lake Mountains. While in position and conformation they appear to be part of the Madison Range, the Henry's Lake Mountains are different, as will be explained

later. In the meantime, a mention of the "Madison Range" will include the Henry's Lake formation.

Slightly less than two miles southwest from the canyon mouth and the Madison Range fault scarp, across the Madison Valley, lie Cliff and Wade lakes, which were affected in different ways by the Hebgen quake. The lakes are long, narrow bodies of water lying end to end in a cleft on the west side of the Madison Valley. It has been suggested that this trench may once have been the course of the Madison River, when the river flowed around the southern end of the Madison Range (or the Henry/s Lake Mountains) and before it carved Madison Canyon.

The north end of Cliff Lake subsided perhaps two feet relative to the rest of the lake, judging by changes in the shoreline. Wade, north of Cliff, reportedly was higher after the quake but without apparent tilting. But unlike Hebgen Lake, which had old survey benchmarks all along its northern shoreline, there was no way to measure either subsidence or uplift from pre-quake elevation at Wade or Cliff.

This Cliff Lake tilt, having the same northwestern dip as the Hebgen Lake tilt, hints at a connection and is a factor in possible expansion of the area involved, as Hamilton contends.

Like Earthquake Lake, rockslides in prehistoric times formed both Wade and Cliff lakes, on a bench rising up from the west side of the Madison River Valley. It is an area shaped by numerous slides, according to J. Michael O'Neill of the USGS, working out of Denver. A map showing faults and landslides in the area, prepared by O'Neill, Thomas H. LeRoy and Paul E. Carrara, was published by the USGS in 1994. One of the old slides shown briefly dammed the Madison River in the valley, approximately 8 miles downstream from the landslide which created Earthquake Lake.

Conflicting Interpretations

I invite you to shift perspective for a moment.

Thus far, we have explored the Hebgen faulting and resulting quake as centered in the West Yellowstone basin, most intensely in an area bounded between Highway 20 and the town of West Yellowstone on the south and southeast, the low hills above the 1959 epicenter on the northeast, by Beaver Creek on the northwest, and by Kirkwood Ridge on the north — plus part of the Madison Range and the Missouri Flats area immediately west of the range.

This interpretation of the quake is largely that of Irving J. Witkind and colleagues George D. Fraser and Willis H. Nelson, who wrote the paper "A Geological Interpretation of the Epicentral Area — The Dual-Basin Concept" for USGS's 242-page technical report on the quake, published in 1964 as Professional Paper 435. Fraser and Nelson, now deceased, were part of the first wave of U. S. Geological Survey teams who descended on the area following the quake.

Describing a different concept were W. Bradley Myers (deceased) and Warren Hamilton. They also were among the federal geologists immediately dispatched to the area. Hamilton is a "distinguished senior scientist" in the Dept. of Geophysics at Colorado School of Mines and still is an active researcher in global tectonics.

"Perhaps it would be best to discuss this under the heading of 'Ten Geologists, Ten Interpretations,'" writes Epstein of the controversy which started brewing during his rookie year between Witkind, his boss, and Hamilton. "Interpretations of geologic events are often similar to the forensic science applied in our court system.

"Surface geologic evidence for any event is generally limited. Bedrock exposures may vary from excellent in desert terrains to less than 1 percent in areas covered by vegetations and soil. Subsurface data may be non-existent or limited. Interpretation of these data will be deduced by the individual according to his or her educational background and field experience … Each geologist must, of necessity, have a different bag of experiences.

"One of the controversies that emerged … relates to the number of 'basins' that dropped due to the tectonic deformation, and the pattern of subsidence that was produced. Subsidence … was irregular and included the West Yellowstone basin, the Madison Range to the west, and the Missouri Flats immediately west of the Madison Range.

"One group of geologists (led by Witkind) favored a 'dual basin' interpretation, whereby the Madison Range did not subside, but the two areas on either side did. Opposing this view is the 'single basin hypothesis' (proposed by Myers and Hamilton) which suggests that this entire area, including the Madison Range, sank as a single, albeit irregular, block," but dropping much less than the West Yellowstone basin.

Alluding to his court decision analogy, Epstein concludes, "The trial took place in several peer-reviewed journal articles, but the jury is still out. Can a hypothetical jury make a reasonable judgment, beyond a reasonable doubt? Probably not."

Among the differences between their conclusions is how a subsidence that bridged the Madison Range affected the mountains themselves. There were no pre-quake or new elevation measurements on which to base a finding either way, both agreed.

A phenomenon they could measure and evaluate — but for years differed about — was the highway elevation change along the north shore of Hebgen Lake and beyond, downstream from the dam. Witkind saw a greater role of quake-caused soil compaction as he read elevation changes, and pointed out that surface differences may not accurately reflect what happened in the bedrock below as it fractured.

"Myers and I argued," says Hamilton, "that the major system now, starting only recently in geologic time, is southward tilting in the region toward faulting on the north slopes of the Centennial Mountains. We saw Hebgen as a sideshow conflict between old and new systems." Hamilton estimated the Centennials rose up less than a million years ago.

When I interviewed Hamilton and Wit, the passage of nearly 50 years had not diminished the strength of either man's opinions, but the two spoke civilly of one another. Only another earthquake, perhaps, can settle their differences.

Other Slides

The large Madison Canyon slide had smaller versions throughout the area.

The largest, mentioned earlier in describing the lake's tilt, was near Hilgard Resort, the point of greatest measured subsidence. The slide started about 100 feet above Hebgen Lake level and carried 1,000 feet of highway and 350,000 cubic yards of earth beneath the surface of the lake. This slide and others in the area occurred only on colluvial material on slopes greater than 10 degrees which extended below lake level.

98

Similar slopes even nearer to the fault scarp, if not lubricated by water, did not slide.

Because of such slides and the lake's northward tilt, the Montana Highway Department had to rebuild the highway along the north shore. Nearly everyone was a bit gun-shy.

An engineer needed help to rough out a possible new route, so invited rancher Gerald Yetter to join him. As Yetter recalls it: "We paced off a distance up from the lake and were about to set some stakes when an aftershock hit. The engineer said, 'Well, let's go up another hundred yards.' So we did. And about the time we were hammering some new stakes, another one hit. And the engineer jokingly says, 'Well, that's enough for me. Maybe we should bring the road down off the top of that ridge.'"

The most common types of landslide were the numerous rockfalls. Cliffs of volcanic rocks in the western part of Yellowstone National Park and along Cliff and Wade lakes — at the eastern and western ends of the subsidence area — were particularly affected. Large blocks of welded rhyolite tuff, some up to 20 feet on a side, tumbled off canyon walls above the lakes and caused the only fatalities outside the Madison slide area. "These blocks fell in large numbers during the earthquake, smashing large trees on the slopes below and coming to rest in some places amid great piles of similar blocks which had preceded them in past centuries," Hadley wrote.

Unusual among the various landslides was the Kirkwood mudflow (Fig. 29). It involved a section of land 400 to 800 feet wide and half a mile long, located in the Kirkwood Creek drainage on the mountainside northeast of Hebgen Lake. It started sliding five days after the quake and was still moving a month later, with a displacement of at least 100 feet. It was an old slide which had been inactive for many years.

Jack Epstein described the eerie sensation of standing on the flow, hearing trees crack and then seeing them slowly bend over as their underpinnings slumped downhill.

One possible cause of the flow reactivation may have been the increased flow of groundwater in much of the quake area after the initial shock, thus lubricating the slide. Still another phenomenon of the quake was discovery of "churned ground" — when soil and objects such as rocks resting on it are thrown into the air or overturned with little horizontal displacement. These dislocations apparently result from ground vibrations whose vertical movements exceed that of gravity. Near one ridge crest strewn with frost-heaved limestone blocks, 95 percent of the stones had been overturned so that their gray, weathered, (former) upper sides were underneath and their yellowish undersides, formerly buried, were now on top. Geologists also found sections of soil several inches thick that had been overturned with leaves of alpine plants underneath and their roots extending upward into the air.

Churned ground was found only where bedrock was exposed, not over thick layers of soil or great depths of loose rock. Hamilton wrote: "The restriction of the churned areas to small isolated parts of the many bedrock exposures in the epicentral area suggests not only that seismic waves traveled along strong bedrock units and emerged at the surface with little loss of energy, but also that they may have been reinforced locally by interference of two or more waves."

Sand spouts, or "earthquake fountains," were among the phenomena analyzed by Frank A. Swenson of the USGS. Those occurring at the lower end of Beaver Creek ejected ground water under pressure sufficient to tear loose sections of sod, six to eight inches thick and several feet square, and toss them aside. Sand spouts, often forming crater-like rings of sand, also were found along the northeastern shore of Hebgen Lake and on Horse Butte peninsula between the Grayling and Madison arms of the lake. Some even showed up on the lake bed, discovered when the reservoir was lowered in the spring of 1960 for repair of the dam, one crater being 10 feet in diameter and three feet deep.

The Lake Bottom

Because of the major land deformations along the northeastern shore of Hebgen Lake, a detailed survey of the lake bottom was undertaken in September 1959, studying the entire length of the lake. The lake was traversed from shore to shore, measuring depths with an acoustic echo sounder. These soundings gave no indication of major faulting on the lake bottom.

Equipment was mounted on a small boat powered by an outboard motor. A sonic depth recorder converts electrical energy to sound and transmits it downward. When the energy strikes the bottom or any other object with acoustic properties different from those of water, part of the signal is reflected back as an echo.

A pre-dam survey by Montana Power Company, in 1906, provided the only data available showing land contours prior to lake formation. Wayne H. Jackson of the USGS reported that the greatest change in the lake bottom was within two miles of Hebgen Dam where the quake slumped landslide debris at least 16 feet deep into the deepest part of the lake. Subsidence of the floor occurred and tilting was found.

Water Flow Changes

Water flow changes were documented in various categories by several investigators.

Storage capacity of Hebgen Lake, due to its subsidence, increased by 9,000 acre feet, or 2 percent. This change, however, was a function of the reservoir's new shape rather than increased flow into the Madison watershed.

Some streams in the area temporarily increased flow immediately after the quake, the Madison River by 41 percent near West Yellowsone and the Gardiner River near Mammoth Hot Springs by about 50 percent. Computed average flow into Hebgen Lake increased by 80 percent from the first half of August 1959 to the last half of the month, after the quake, with little or no rain contributing

Most streams are spring fed, but after the quake most of these springs became very turbid. Some springs increased flow, others decreased or ceased. Temperature rose in some springs and new thermal springs arose from an active fault zone.

Of the approximately 600 well water recorders throughout the United States operated then by the USGS, 185 showed water level fluctuations, up or down, caused by the Hebgen quake. Maximum fluctuation exceeded 10 feet. Fluctuations exceeded 12 inches in wells in nine states and 6-12 inches in wells in 5 states. Fluctuations, although small, were recorded in wells as far away as Puerto Rico and Hawaii.

Other than increased water turbidity, a study of chemical quality of ground water showed no alarming abnormalities.

Yellowstone Thermal Changes

Geysers and other thermal features in nearby Yellowstone National Park have long been closely observed and measured. Millions of park visitors expect Old Faithful to be faithful, thus its name, or at least be regular. And how did the Hebgen Lake earthquake affect the world's largest and hottest concentration of thermal attractions?

A hurried inspection of the geyser basins was top priority in the park at first light on Aug. 18, 1959. One of these scientists was George D. Marler of the National Park Service, who reported on thermal effects for the USGS Professional Paper 435.

The first erupting geyser he saw was Giantess, in the Upper Geyser Basin near Old Faithful. Up to then, Giantess had erupted only twice that year, in March and May.

Now, jets of water appearing 100 feet high were arcing out and away from the crater. Instead of this water phase lasting the usual 24 or 26 hours, Marler wrote in his detailed 1973 "Inventory of Thermal Features of the Firehole River Geyser Basins and Other Selected Areas of Yellowstone National Park," it continued constantly for four days, more than 100 hours. And he didn't even see it start.

"I marveled at where all the energy and water were coming from. The longest known duration of any previous eruption was 38 hours."

Until 1973, only 1964 went without a Giantess eruption. In the ten years prior to 1973, the geyser's 20 eruptions topped any previous decade back to the creation of the National Park Service, perhaps even to 1870, he wrote.

Old Faithful seemed for several days to have survived the 1959 quake without change. Intervals between eruptions were erratic, but such phases were not unusual. As time went on, however, intervals lengthened by December to 67.4 minutes compared with an average of 61.8 minutes in the summer months just preceding the quake. The interval now has increased even more to roughly 80 minutes.

Only one of the large geysers was affected adversely. Grand Geyser erupted immediately after the quake but then became dormant. Previously it exhibited 10-hour intervals. However, other geysers near Grand played on shortened intervals and one previously dormant spring started erupting enthusiastically.

Sapphire Pool erupted every 17 to 20 minutes to a height of three to six feet before the quake. From August to September it constantly surged 6 to 8 feet high. Starting Sept. 5, 1959, following a strong tremor the night before, Sapphire's steady boiling and surging became periodic but regular, occurring at two-hour intervals. Eruptions were spectacular, however, rising 150 feet high and 200 feet wide at the base.

Changes were particularly significant along the Firehole River drainage, the region of Yellowstone's most famous features. Scores of geysers and quiescent springs began erupting. A few new geysers were born. Some hot springs were adversely affected but overall there seemed to be increased thermal activity.

An earthquake may be the reason we have Old Faithful at all. The geyser issues from a large crack that crosses its mound. Marler, in 1956, wrote for the *American Journal of Science* that the direct precursor to Old Faithful "built the terraces and interred the stumps (and only) began to flow when some 'mechanical adjustment' (such as a quake) broke the geyserite

shield, thereby tapping arteries that had been sealed off in their upper reaches."

Marler, no doubt, was pleased three years later to be able to write for the USGS: "Effects of the Hebgen Lake earthquake do much to confirm this (previous) speculation on the genesis of Old Faithful."

The quake made no observed change to one of my favorites, Lone Star Geyser, a pleasant hike off the highway near Old Faithful. It is at the base of a large moraine, an elongated mound of earth and rock carried and pushed there thousands of years ago by a now-extinct glacier. Lone Star is a successor to hot springs buried during the glacial period. Several other moraines lie in a direct one-mile progression to the north. Marler wrote that the moraines apparently rest across an old fissure which is less active today than it was preceding the ice advance.

Grand Prismatic Spring, an unusually large and colorful spring in Midway Geyser Basin, apparently tilted in the 1959 quake. Water was found to be flowing only over the eastern rim of the crater, while usually it flowed evenly over the rim on all sides. But in 1961 Grand Prismatic resumed its previous flow all around its 300-foot diameter. It either had returned to its previous levelness or increased its outflow to pre-quake volume, an estimated 560 gallons per minute.

Marler's otherwise seriously presented descriptions include this amusing story: The night of the Hebgen quake a husband and wife were skinny-dipping in Bath Spring, named for its suitability for bathing at body-heat temperature. They were quite relaxed in the comforting water, located near Madison Junction, when a big tremor hit and the pool suddenly drained, quickly and completely. Others, apparently waiting their turn in the pool, verified the story. The Park service frowns on the practice of "hot potting" and has tried to eliminate it, for the preservation of the park as well as for people's safety.

Checking the Basement

How far back — that is, how far down through the rock layers of time — must we go to better understand how this terrain developed its present appearance?

Witkind and colleagues Hadley and Willis H. Nelson studied rocks formed in pre-Tertiary time, meaning prior to dinosaur extinction about 65 million years ago. The oldest rocks exposed in the Hebgen Lake area are dolomite, schist, gneiss, amphibolite and quartzite more than two billion years old. Covering this basement of metamorphic rocks, which had been changed when hot and deep, are various layers of sedimentary rocks laid down when seas covered much of what is now central North America, during the Paleozoic and Mesozoic eras from 550 to 65 million years ago. These sedimentary rocks are largely limestones, shales, sandstones, mudstones, and conglomerates. Oldest in the Hebgen area is the Madison Limestone, 1,450 feet thick and 350 to 300 million years old, and the most recent, the Colorado Group of shales and sandstones, which is approximately 2,500 feet thick and 150 to 65 million years old — formed in the heyday of dinosaurs.

Think of this land as long having been almost flat. Huge inland seas settle out precipitated calcium carbonate (the remains of aquatic creatures), and clay and silt and sand has washed out from the land. Layers are compacted and hardened and often extend for hundreds of miles. Of course, shoreline configuration of these pre-historic seas can change over time or, as we have seen at Hebgen, on a moment's notice.

Several periods of mountain-building, called orogenies, shaped the western states. Compression caused rock layers to fold and buckle upward, then fracture or fault and rise from compacting pressures again and again. The three major periods of this surface deformation were the Nevadan orogeny, the Sevier orogeny and finally the Laramide orogeny. Madison and Gallatin ranges of the Hebgen area stem from the Laramide age, starting 80 to 70 million years ago and ending 55 to 35 million years ago. An epoch of late Tertiary faulting and basin formation, perhaps the last 30 million years, was imposed on top of Laramide regional folds and thrust faults.

Viewing the length of Hebgen Lake, toward the northwest, your sight line is up the large Beaver Creek drainage and nearly parallel to the ridge line of the Madison Range to your left. Cabin Creek and the Gallatin Range veer off toward the north. All three drainages — the Madison plus Beaver and Cabin creeks — join a short distance below Hebgen Dam. Near this convergence the Madison River cuts a radically new direction, directly southwest through the Madison Range. It is an antecedent canyon in that the stream downcutting has kept pace with upfaulting of the Madison Range.

Sagging of the West Yellowstone basin toward the northwest has continued over a long period of time. Hamilton and Myers found evidence of several basin streams whose routes migrated north, toward this subsidence. At least part of the basin probably once drained northeast into the Gallatin River. Headwaters of the Gallatin and for Grayling Creek are quite close together inside the northwest corner of the park. Their watersheds split, the Gallatin flowing north and Grayling south into Hebgen Lake.

Hamilton and Myers also proposed that the West Yellowstone basin at one time emptied in the other direction, southward into the Snake River drainage. Rimming the southern side of the basin are huge flows of late Quarternary rhyolite hundreds of feet thick. The flow immediately south of the town of West

Yellowstone is more recent than Bull Lake glaciation. Before being blocked by these volcanic eruptions, Hamilton wrote, the West Yellowstone basin drained south and west around the south end of the Madison Range to the Snake, thence west toward the Pacific rather than to the Atlantic via the Madison, Missouri, and Mississippi rivers as now.

An ancestral north fork of the Snake River probably headed in the Beaver Creek drainage. Repeated subsidence of the basin as well as what is now the Madison Canyon reversed the drainage from south around the end of the mountains to the line southwest directly through the Madison Range.

Another reading of the terrain theorized that the West Yellowstone basin was once a very large natural lake, unaided by any man-made dam. W. C. Alden, in USGS professional Paper 231, 1953, "Physiography and Glacial Geology of Western Montana and Adjacent Areas," cited the post-Bull Lake glaciers which chewed out the canyon of Beaver Creek, leaving a large terminal moraine. This moraine mound now is some 300 feet high and crowds the Madison River over against the south wall of its canyon. The moraine was referenced earlier as the location of Refuge Point.

This moraine and its glacier may have formed a temporary dam that ponded the river as far back as the western edge of the park. Alden said the presence of stratified rhyolite sand in the West Yellowstone basin indicates that a lake once existed there. The theory is controversial because a number of other processes could have formed the basin.

According to O'Neill, nearly all of southwestern Montana's streams at some time have changed direction to flow north instead of south. Some even gouged canyons through substantial mountain ranges to accomplish the change, such as the Madison

here near Hebgen and again, north of Ennis, where the river cuts through Bear Trap Canyon

Faults, Then Earthquakes

What about earthquakes prior to 1959? We need to look back further in time, as David Schwartz has. As part of his earthquake hazards studies, Schwartz presented a report of his Hebgen Lake research at the Seismic Summit in Reno, NV, in 2004.

Schwartz and his colleagues trenched down far enough to document the occurrence of the two most recent Hebgen earthquakes prior to 1959 — one 1,000 to 3,000 years ago and an earlier quake 7,000 to 13,500 years ago. Schwartz and his team found that these pre-historic quakes occurred in the same place and produced an amount of displacement similar to the 1959 event.

They found that the slip rate of these faults between quakes has been accelerating, nearly doubling. The average slippage for the whole period, from the oldest to the 1959 event, was 0.8 millimeters per year, compared with 1.5 millimeters per year from the middle documented event up to the most recent.

Earlier quakes definitely hit Hebgen, Schwartz says, but his team did not trench deeply enough to find direct evidence of them.

Schwartz cites earlier work by seismologist Doser who proposed in 1985 that the Red Canyon fault is the primary structure and that the Hebgen fault splits off from it (Fig. 25). Red Canyon's big curve and its apparent split with the Hebgen make this a complex fault system, in contrast to the nearby

Madison Range fault scarp which is virtually straight and level for much of its 40-mile length.

Fault scarps tend to fade from prominence over time as erosion wears them down and new plant growth invades their slopes. I accompanied Schwartz, his colleague in the USDA, Suzanne Hecker, and Francesca Cinti, a geologist who researches active tectonics and paleoseismology for the Instituto Nazionale di Geofisica e Vulcanologia in Rome, Italy, as they re-visited the Hebgen and Red Canyon scarps in September 2008, searching for further evidence of pre-1959 quakes. Everywhere they looked along those scarps they found signs of earlier faulting, Schwartz said.

In many cases, however, surface traces of major earth movement nearly vanish.

Time Stacked on Edge

As one gazes at the southern end of the Madison Range from the southwest side, you see a string of peaks around 11,000 feet in elevation, divided by high mountain passes that are mostly 7,600 to 8,000 feet in elevation. You the viewer stand in the Madison Valley more than 4,000 feet below the peaks.. The mountain range before you runs from north, on your left, to south.

There is one exception, however, to this typical peak-pass-peak-pass pattern and that is the Madison Canyon. The canyon starts on the far side of the mountains where the Madison River discharges out of Hebgen Lake before cutting through the mountains toward us to exit into the Madison Valley. What sort of geologic processes, or series of events, caused such a break through what once was a solid range of mountains?

O'Neill believes repeated faulting — on the same southwest-northeast line as the canyon — opened the door for other geologic forces such as erosion and possibly glacial grinding to create Madison Canyon, directly through the Madison Range.

I invite you for a moment to look down upon it. You could do that with a topographic map of the region, seeing the points of peaks, the relief of level places, and the straight or meandering course of creeks and rivers. Elevations printed on prominent locations give clues about terrain, but soon the swirls and distances between the topographic lines — lines closer together mean steeper slopes — start to make sense and paint a picture.

There is yet another sedentary way to look at this area, whether speaking of human behavior or geological formations.

Spread a geologic map out on the living room floor — namely the *Geologic Map of the Hebgen Lake Quadrangle,*, published by the USGS in 2004 — and you see an intriguing abstract of color, each individual hue and its family of colors representing different rock formations and periods of time in which these earth-building materials collected. (A small version of this map is printed on the inside back cover.)

The map's authors are USGS geologists O'Neill and Robert L. Christiansen, the latter now retired. In addition to their own field work, they compiled the surveys accomplished by some twenty other geologists, completed mostly since the 1959 quake.

The newest material to arrive on the scene are the silts, sands, gravels, clays and volcanic debris which also cover a substantial part of the map's lowlands, or anywhere the force that carried them slowed or stopped and thus dropped them. These are the materials dislodged from their starting point at higher elevations and were brought down by water erosion, glacial movement, succumbing to gravity, or volcanic activity — or all four. These are called surficial deposits, geologic jargon for surface. Emplacement happened any time from the mountain snow runoff last spring to at least 23 million years ago. The map shows these in various shades of yellow and tan.

The next section represents igneous rocks, or the rhyolites, basalts, welded tuffs, ash, and other material emplaced by volcanic flows or explosive upheaval. This period also goes back as much as 23 million years. But the most recent volcanic activity was about 70,000 years ago. These are indicated in pinks, reds and purples.

Even older are the granite and the sedimentary rocks — shales, sandstones, limestones, schists, and some of the dolomite. When were these water-borne sediments laid down? Start about 23 million years ago in the Miocene epoch, when modern mammal and bird families became recognizable, and go back to 513 million years ago, to the Middle Cambrian, when the seas were the home of most animals, such as Trilobites and sponges. Key colors for these rocks are browns, greens, blues, reds and oranges.

This Hebgen area has even older rocks, from the late Paleoproterozoic era of approximately 1.8 billion years ago back further to the middle Archean era approximately 3.2 billion years ago, the time of earliest known fossils of once-living creatures. These are metamorphic rocks — some beginning as igneous material in a molten state, some beginning as sedimentary layers — which have changed form due to heat and pressure. Code these in dark earth colors, such as olive drab, gray, or dark, dusky blue.

We need to focus on just one of these rock types, a formation of dolomitic marble, or dolomite, which played a role in both the Madison Canyon slide and the survival of Hebgen Dam. This dolomite is approximately 2.5 billion years old.

The USGS geologic map shows a series of rock strata that stand on edge near the south end of the Madison Range, where the Madison River cuts through. Picture a loaf of sliced bread on your kitchen counter, one heel toward the northwest, the other pointing to the southeast, representing the Madison Range. One of these slices represents a very thin layer of dolomite, the same structure that partially collapsed in the Hebgen quake and allowed the slide at Rock Creek near the mouth of the canyon. Its color is a deep, dusky blue on the map. It outcrops along the course of the Madison River and Canyon. Only part of it fractured. Not bad for being 2.5 billion years old!

TIME OUT: We are talking here about a canyon splitting a long mountain range. North of the canyon it's always been known as the Madison Range. South of the canyon it's now called the Henry's Lake Mountains. Most people could never tell the difference from just looking. And on the surface, even the geologic map seems to accentuate the mountains' continuity.

But the rocks are different, says O'Neill — the really old rocks in the Henry's Lake section, and the really, really, really old rocks (about 3 billion years old) in the Madison Range to the north. O'Neill quickly adds, however, that this is one of those areas where geology's usual bottom-equals-oldest-and-top-equals-youngest reckoning of rocks' age needs modification because of the complex upheavals of the topography.

"In the field, the first thing I do is determine which way is up, as shown in the rocks," O'Neill says, "but here it's all jumbled. The oldest rocks have metamorphosed so much they have lost all signs of what they once were."

O'Neill believes these "slices" of rock have been in place on edge at least 1.8 billion years. Much later, during the Laramide Orogeny's compression of the terrain, they were uplifted, then uplifted again during the Basin and Range period of stretching basins and rising mountains.

"I guess the important thing is, there are three or four different faults that run beneath and downstream from Hebgen Dam," O'Neill says. "Those are the faults responsible for controlling the course of the Madison River.

"The river went through that gap because the faults were there.

"There was enough breaking of rock — cataclasis is the word geologists use — to make it easier for the river to transgress through and create that canyon."

In other words, these rocks formed, reformed, tilted, rose up, jumbled, lifted again, split apart, fell, eroded, and decomposed long before the Hebgen quake and the Madison slide jolted our attention to them.

A few "slices" to the southeast on the Henry's Lake Mountains — each slice representing a different type of rock — is another blue stripe indicating a much larger dolomite formation a mile or more thick, that is, wide, since it is uplifted vertically from its original horizontal (sedimentary) plane of formation. The dolomite slice spans the breadth of the range, from Reynolds Pass on the southwest end to Hebgen Dam on the northeast. There it forms the southwest abutment of the dam, constitutes the bedrock on which the dam is built, and even emerges again between the northeast end of the dam and the Hebgen fault scarp 1,000 feet beyond.

As the dam dropped 9.5 feet — and we know that the lake, the Hebgen fault, and the mountainside above it all dropped — one wonders whether the huge, mile thick and 11-mile long slice of dolomite dropped by a similar amount. Certainly the northeast end of it dropped that much. We know the survey benchmark near the dam subsided by 9.5 feet, and the dam

and its abutments at both ends and the lake all appear to have dropped equally as a unit.

Amazing! The Hebgen faulting and quake gave us a modern-day view of Earth's ancient building processes. While the dolomite and slices of other rock types were originally formed in a horizontal position, their now steeply dipping aspect appears as if some giant pair of hands laid the loaf of horizontal slices over on it side, raising the slices to nearly vertical.

Tilting of these old rocks first occurred as long ago as 2.5 billion years. Subsequently, the dolomite and related rocks were uplifted again during the period of mountain-building known as the Laramide Orogeny. It came in short, sudden bursts of faulting and earthquake activity sometime in the late Cretaceous period, 70 to 80 million years ago.

Not only did this process uplift the whole range, O'Neill points out, but it pushed this dolomite and other old rocks over to the northeast, on top of much younger sedimentary formations. This overlay can be seen in the area of Hebgen Dam and the Hebgen fault scarp, where geologists find 2.5 billion-year-old dolomite on top of rocks one-fifth as ancient.

And these rocks and earth are still rearranging themselves — sometimes quickly, but usually very, very gradually. What conclusions about the Madison Canyon slide might be made by some investigator a million years from now?

Terrain Shaped Again by Volcanism

Volcanic activity is still another geologic phenomenon that has formed this region. The most spectacular of these events were the huge caldera-forming super volcanoes associated with what is now called the "Yellowstone hot spot." The future of volcanism — its possible immanence and the dangers of its reemergence — are discussed later in Chapter 11. But let's look at what has happened thus far.

The West Yellowstone basin and some of the surrounding mountains are covered with volcanic material of various sorts, some old and some relatively young. Some of the product of the oldest volcanism is welded rhyolite tuff, explosively erupted volcanic ash and larger particles that were hot enough to weld together when they landed. Some is dated back to Oligocene time, or approximately 23 to 33 million years ago.

Dating formations by layered position is not the only method. The Oligocene date was determined by tree plant pollen specimens identified by Estella B. Leopold. She found siltstones along a logging road 6 miles west of West Yellowstone holding pollen counts as high as 500 grains per gram. Leopold identified conifers such as pine, fir and hemlock, broadleaf trees such as hickory, lingnut, walnut, birch, alder, elm and holly, as well as other unclassified specimens.

Leopold said the discovery clearly indicated a moist-temperate climate — much different from today's cooler, arid weather conditions which could not support many of those species.

The most recent lava flow described was huge, coming up from the south to cover 80 square miles of the West Yellowstone basin and advancing to within four miles of what became the town of West Yellowstone. The flow had a volume calculated at five to 10 cubic miles of rhyolite. Distinctive columnar cliffs mark the northeastern extent of the flow at Lower Geyser Basin and the west wall of Firehole Canyon.

Geologist Hamilton, who traveled worldwide studying volcanism in the years following his work in the Yellowstone region, dated this flow as definitely within the Pleistocene interglacial period. And what is that? First there was gravel laid down by Bull Lake glaciation, which began 200,000 years ago and ended about 130,000 years ago. Then came this enormous lava flow, which occurred during a much warmer interglacial period of roughly 60,000 years, preceding advance of still another Glacial period known as the Pinedale.

Hamilton dates this flow, the most recent volcanism known, as approximately 70,000 years old. That places it within a Pleistocene interglacial interval — both preceded and succeeded by ice, the Bull Lake glaciation before and the Pinedale glaciation after. The sequence recalls Robert Frost's poem *Fire and Ice:*

> *Some say the world will end in fire,*
> *Some say in ice.*
> *From what I've tasted of desire*
> *I hold with those who favor fire.*
> *But if it had to perish twice,*
> *I think I know enough of hate*
> *To say that for destruction ice*
> *Is also great*
> *And would suffice.*

Destruction? Construction? Occurring simultaneously?

Re-Shaped by Glaciation

Glacial ice has advanced at least three times to re-shape the West Yellowstone basin, grinding down across the Gallatin Range and Yellowstone (Park) Plateau from the high Absaroka Mountains to the northeast. Erratics — that is, rocks found as aliens out of their original context and therefore moved from somewhere else — are found at 9,525 feet elevation, suggesting that, in one early glacial period, ice was essentially continuous from the Absaroka Range to the crest of the Madison Range.

Glaciers are dated and identified by the debris they leave behind.

Some of the earliest glacial remains found in the West Yellowstone basin are from the Teton mountains to the southeast and date back 1.5 million years, separate but equivalent in age to glaciation which covered the Midwest out of Canada.

In the center of the West Yellowstone basin lies Horse Butte, located near the tip of a peninsula which separates the two main arms of Hebgen Lake (Fig. 2). A large glacial moraine complex extends nearly across The Narrows on the north side of Hebgen Lake, wraps around the northwest end of Horse Butte, forms a second moraine nearly across the Madison Arm of the lake and overlaps a rocky promontory on the lake's southern shore. The two moraines look alike, but their rocks indicate two distinct stages of the ice advance known as Bull Lake glaciation, mentioned earlier as part of the glacial gravel sandwich encasing a huge lava flow.

In general, however, Bull Lake glaciation flowed out of the park onto the basin as far as The Narrows and Horse Butte.

Following the Bull Lake period came the Pinedale, which lasted from about 30,000 to 10,000 years ago and was at its peak between 23,500 and 21,000 years ago. In other words, glacial sculpting of this terrain came at a time the first humans were migrating to the Americas, with arrival theories ranging from 50,000 to 11,000 years ago. During this same time range, early humans were creating beautiful cave art at Lascaux and other locations in France, 32,000 to 10,000 years ago.

It was Pinedale-era glaciers which were responsible for damming Lake Missoula several times, eventually melting and breaking free to loose periodic massive floods through northern Idaho, Spokane, Washington, and across the eastern Washington scablands to the Columbia River. Remnants of the flood are found as far away as the Willamette River south of Portland.

Pinedale glaciers left three sets of moraines to mark their furthest westward progress. Each subsequent advance ended further east inside the park. Ice of the first Pinedale advance rose from 6,000 feet elevation at its Horse Butte terminus to 7,250 feet where it crossed the mouth of Gibbon Canyon, a distance of nearly 20 miles. Its ice once was approximately 600 feet thick over the present site of Old Faithful Geyser. During the third and final Pinedale glaciation, ice persisted only in the Yellowstone Lake basin at an altitude of about 8,000 feet.

Since the last glacier, some 10,000 years ago, the major observable change to this West Yellowstone basin terrain has been from erosion, construction of Hebgen Dam enlarging the lake, of course the 1959 earthquake, and its predecessor 1-3,000 years before.

Measuring Earth Movement

One of the first things asked after an earthquake hits is, "How strong was it?"

By that, most people want to know how violently the earth shook, or the magnitude of the quake. And they immediately want to start comparing it to other seismic events.

It depends upon which scale you're using.

Not until 1935, when Charles F. Richter in collaboration with Beno Gutenberg at California Institute of Technology,

108

developed the Richter Magnitude Scale, did we have a reliable, quantitative system for measuring earthquakes.

Until Richter, the world relied on the Mercalli Intensity Scale, developed in 1902 by Giuseppe Mercalli, which rates quakes by human observation of how intensely the shaking was felt, what damage to buildings occurred, and the distance/range away from the location of such damage. Obviously, this produced subjective evaluations and high variability.

Such anecdotal accounts, as found in the first part of this book — including the first reactions of geologists camped near Hebgen that night — fall into the Mercalli category. Most of the press coverage and books about the event also focused on human observation.

People experience phenomena differently, which is not to say inaccurately.

Richter and Gutenberg developed a 1.0 to 12.0 scale to measure earth movement from the length of squiggles traced by the earth's vibrations on a seismograph. When the bolted-down seismograph frame moves with the earth — during a quake, or even when a heavy truck drives by — a heavy pendulum suspended in the seismograph tends to remain stationary. This differential between the stable and moving parts is mechanically transmitted to a slowly moving roll of graph paper. *Voila*. A quantitative record. Day after day the seismograph's tracing barely moves off the center-line of the graph. Then there is a flurry of minor activity showing, but we learn it was merely the movement of heavy machinery nearby. But one day the squiggles left and right of center — such as the Hebgen quake seismograph on our book's cover — come fast and heavy indicating a quake. Earth scientists roll into action.

The Hebgen Lake quake initially rated 7.1 on the Richter scale. Subsequent study and collection of evidence from a broader array of seismographs moved this rating up to 7.3, then 7.5. Because of the logarithmic basis of the scale, this means the quake's magnitude of movement was four times as great as originally thought.

Thus each whole number increase on the scale, from 3.0 to 4.0 for instance, represents a tenfold increase in earth movement, or amplitude on the seismograph.

Another measure of earthquakes is to estimate the amount of energy released, as in the Moment Magnitude Scale (MMS) developed in 1979 by Harvard University seismologists Thomas C. Hanks and Hiroo Kanamori. They and others had realized that the Richter was not reliable for quakes over 7 or for measurements taken 350 miles or more from the quake's epicenter.

In scientific circles, "moment magnitude" is now the most commonly used measure for medium to large quakes, but not for quakes of 3.5 magnitude or less. Richter remains the standard for these smaller quakes, which constitute the great majority of seismic events.

The 7.5 Richter rating for Hebgen is 7.3 in moment magnitude. Following are comparisons of other major earthquakes: San Francisco in 1906, moment magnitude 7.9 instead of 8.0 Richter; Chilean in 1960, 9.6 instead of 9.0; Anchorage in 1964, 9.2 instead of 8.5.

We have chosen to use Richter because the public is more familiar with it, the media more commonly refer to it, and, obviously, the numbers are close. But despite scientific agencies such as the USGS usually using moment magnitude, many people will automatically think Richter because it has become almost a household word.

While the scale numbers will remain similar, Richter measures the amplitude of earth movement and moment magnitude measures released energy. A quake of 4 Richter is 10 times the magnitude of measured amplitude (movement) as a 3. On both scales, each whole number increase in the magnitude scale corresponds to the release of about 31 times more energy than the preceding whole number value.

A Mercalli-type measure of quake intensity was given years ago by Leonard M. Murphy and Rutledge J. Brazee, both of the USGS, when they reported that the Hebgen quake was felt over an area of 600,000 square miles, from Utah and Nevada to British Columbia, and from the Pacific coast to western North Dakota.

Thus we evaluate earthquakes by intensity (what is observed), by magnitude of amplitude (earth movement) and moment magnitude (release of energy).

Edmund Christopherson in his book *The Night the Mountain Fell* reported that substantial tremors were felt several days before the Hebgen quake by David Bittner at his lookout post atop 10,300-feet-high Mount Holmes, in the extreme northwest corner of the park. His report was disregarded. But the big quake, having thrown him from his bunk to the floor, convinced Bittner as he picked himself up that his next report to his superiors would be taken more seriously. And it was.

Recorded aftershocks totaled more than 1,300 during the two months through Oct. 15. Of these, 880 came during the first two weeks. By mid-October the rate had dropped to about two per day but immediately after the main shock activity was so constant that precise tabulation for individual shocks was impossible. Information flooded the equipment.

The Hebgen Lake quake is well within a seismically active line running from southern Utah through Salt Lake City, the Teton Range, Yellowstone, Helena, Montana, and Glacier National Park, extending on north into Canada.

What comes next?

The Hebgen and Red Canyon faults are not expected to rupture again for a thousand years or so. But what of the Madison Range fault, a major structural break that has refractured and rehaped its terrain dozens — hundreds, thousands? — of times in the pre-historic past but showed little deformation in 1959?

"There was a small amount of triggered slip on the Madison fault south of Madison Canyon," says Schwartz. "The Madison fault got hit with a substantial amount of stress change, but it is clear that the fault, as a whole, was not ready to go in a large event. It wasn't its time." (See Fig. 50.)

Could it be overdue?

But when is anything really "due?" Taxes. The rent or mortgage payment. In geology, think again. We know certain events are likely to happen again at some point, but not necessarily in our lifetime.

We need to move on and examine other major changes since 1959 in scientific knowledge and technology as well as how we describe natural phenomena and evaluate predictive possibilities.

Chapter 11

Where on Earth Is All This Going?

The flippant, but factual, answer to that question is: Southwest.

That's the direction of movement for the North American plate, a section of the earth's crust that slips about 1.3 inches per year and, as a result, is the prime mover for two highly significant earth-shaping phenomena in the Hebgen-Yellowstone region — earthquakes and volcanism.

The plate has been sliding in that direction at that speed for about 8 million years.

These are the observations of Dr. Robert B. Smith, professor of geology and geophysics at the University of Utah and a driving force of the Yellowstone Volcano Observatory. He began wondering about the plate during his undergraduate days. Smith worked in the back country of Yellowstone National Park early in his career.

Earthquakes result from the stresses and strains in the earth crust's rock base, usually resulting from tectonic plate shift. That's the larger picture. But locally, perhaps a mountain range undergoes further compression and uplift, or a flat basin stretches wider and drops lower. The status quo is broken. Rock strength can no longer resist the stress, and the fracture — a fault — causes an earthquake. When it's over, these rocks return to a relatively stable state until that inch-or-so-a-year plate movement again builds up irresistible stress, in a myriad of fault lines.

Boom. Another fault rupture. Another earthquake, such as depicted by the Hebgen quake's seismograph reproduced on this book's cover.

It could be old faults reactivated — as in the case of Hebgen and Red Canyon — or something new.

Only since the Hebgen earthquake of 1959 has scientific acceptance of plate tectonic theory gathered steam. This understanding of the earth raises particular interest/concern in this Montana-Wyoming-Idaho region because of what is known as the "Yellowstone hot spot," its historic cycle of devastation and Earth remodeling, and, of course, its somewhat uncertain future.

After a natural disaster, whether it's an earthquake, volcano, tornado or hurricane, flood or drought — whatever — we inevitably ask, "When could this happen again?" We are fascinated by forecasts.

Television weather reporters are eager to satisfy this hunger, but for most of the major natural disasters on the menu, scientists are wary of making pinpointed predictions. We are much more apt to hear generalized forecasts or statements about what is "probable" or "likely," in a sense, as odds makers give us the daily line before the Kentucky Derby, or an upcoming Lakers game.

There is little doubt that more earthquakes the size of 1959's Hebgen are likely in some distant timeframe. The region lies in the second most active seismic area in the United States.

Small quakes are not unusual, most of them not felt by humans. Stating a definite timeline for the next big quake, however, is next to impossible and simply is not done.

Asked to predict the next earthquake, geologist Schwartz, of the Earthquake Hazards Program, says — speaking of possibility rather than probability — "The Madison fault could rupture tomorrow but a repeat of 1959 would be unlikely on the Hebgen and Red Canyon for at least another 1,000 years and possibly quite a bit longer. After a major quake, we're usually confident that a fault won't slip again soon."

His USGS office at Menlo Park, California, is located near the San Andreas and numerous other faults in the San Francisco Bay area, for reasons other than convenience to a natural seismic laboratory.

Is he concerned about living and working so close to ground that might split apart beneath him? (He says his home "sits directly up the trend line from the Mount Diablo blind thrust. If you drew a line from where it should come to the surface it almost hits our house.") Apparently that means "no."

"For me, being in the middle of a big earthquake area is obviously exciting," Schwartz says. "The strongest quake I've experienced is the Loma Prieta in '89, which was a 6.9. I fully expect to experience something larger down the road."

Schwartz says he dreams of actually seeing a fault open — "being there."

I ask him about the Hebgen fault being so close to a dam and Schwartz promptly volunteers that he would not live downstream from a dam, whether it's in earthquake country or in terrain with a long history of seismic stability.

Predicting a natural event whose earliest probable reoccurrence is beyond one's own lifetime — perhaps even

beyond civilization as we know it — produces a somewhat empty feeling, one of futility. Worry about it? No. Plan around it? Definitely.

Schwartz, for instance, says he paid more attention to his home's foundation condition and the soil under it than to its location relative to faults.

Now, regarding volcanoes, this must be said: Future volcanic activity in the Yellowstone region is a definite possibility but far from certain.

Volcanoes result when the earth's crust develops a weakness or even a thinning. This combines with a higher-than-usual intrusion of heat from below to create a mixed pool of volcanic material — both molten and solid — near the surface ready to blow, or perhaps just sitting there simmering. Eruptions come as two major types. Lava flows come relatively slowly to form basalt, often cooling and crystallizing to make striking polygonal columns. Or an eruption may come explosively, producing pryoclastic materials with ash-sized to larger particles shooting skyward before falling and, if hot enough, adhering together to form welded tuff. Compared with seismic activity, volcanic eruptions here are much more ancient and less frequent, the most recent of any size here being 70,000 years ago. Nonetheless, subtle changes in the location, shape, and temperature of deep, concentrated masses of hot rock — "anomalies" in the scientific jargon of geophysicists — are closely related to quake activity

If some future eruption is as large and of the same type as three known from Yellowstone's past, it very likely would return the region to wilderness, and certainly not in the current "goodness-what-a-beautiful-national-park" sense. I cannot emphasize too heavily the "if" qualifier.

Past eruptions created vast wilderness no human being has ever seen outside of scientific investigation or speculation or fantasy or a walk on the moon or on Mars. No birds. No bees. No bears. No trees or plants of any kind. No tourists or inhabitants anywhere near for many miles, in any direction you look. Probably not even any traces of old fault scarps. It would be a wasteland. Just rocks and ash.

If you could somehow visit this place after waiting for it to cool down, describing your feeling as "alone" could not begin to describe the experience.

Such barrenness would cover thousands of square miles.

Hear "some day" not as possibly next week or month, but as geologists use the term "recent," meaning a span of a million or so years, plus or minus.

But actually, "some day" could be tomorrow.

Set aside for a moment your understanding of earth change as predominantly a gradual, slow-grinding process covering millennia, and readjust to the idea of instantaneous devastation and cataclysm, such as the Madison Canyon rockslide. It is the same epiphany of time warp Jack Epstein experienced in the day following the Hebgen earthquake watching a falling rock instantly etch scars on a hard cliff surface that could otherwise be interpreted as rock etchings produced by snail-paced glacial grinding.

What we are considering here would be the aftermath of a fourth gigantic volcanic explosion of Yellowstone. Scientists differ about its inevitability.

Geophysicist Smith and the USGS's Robert L. Christiansen, now retired, studied Yellowstone National Park and its volcanic history and future through much of their careers. They are prominent interpreters of the region's geology. Smith's *Windows Into the Earth,* which he wrote with Lee J. Siegel and published in 2000, is a fascinating story of what goes on under Yellowstone's surface, detailed information yet accessible for lay persons. The reader will find Christiansen's most recent work more technically presented. The USGS published it in 2001 as Professional Paper 729-G, *The Quaternary and Pliocene Yellowstone Plateau Volcanic Field of Wyoming, Idaho, and Montana."* Christiansen is lead author, with Smith one of the co-authors, of the 2007 USGS open-file report, *Preliminary Assessment of Volcanic and Hydrothermal Hazards in Yellowstone National Park and Vicinity.*

Underground heat is what makes Yellowstone Yellowstone. A magma chamber, perhaps 5 to 8 miles below the surface, contains solid rock as well as molten material. This hot body of magma is plastic and gradually flows or changes shape under the brittle crust, as it has for millennia. If the magma could be said to have a purpose, it is to sit there heating underground rocks and water above and around it, creating the planet's largest concentration of geysers and other thermal phenomena. Its heat flow into the water and atmosphere circulating from Yellowstone National Park is said to be 30 to 50 times hotter than neighboring areas.

Smith and others believe that movement of the North American plate over a hot spot has created numerous lava flows and eruptions in Yellowstone's past. But here our focus is on the three big ones, separate explosive volcanic eruptions most responsible for the shape of this fascinating land. These were caldera-forming eruptions — explosions which shoot so much buried material into the sky that the overlying crust no longer is supported from below. This crust collapses, creating a caldera, or large crater.

While there are various theories explaining the origin of Yellowstone's high heat, nearly all investigators agree about a relatively shallow magma body below the park and the surface manifestations of the Yellowstone region's explosive volcanic past.

The first super volcano in Yellowstone country was 2 million years ago. Its collapsed surface was several hundred yards deep, the crater about 40 miles wide and 50 miles long, extending from the middle of Yellowstone National Park beyond the southwestern corner of the park into Idaho. It blew out 600 cubic miles of material. Try to picture a pile of ash and rocky fragments as high as an airliner 6 miles up, spreading 10 miles wide and 10 miles long. The blast elevated this material into the atmosphere and winds carried it over much of the western U.S., reaching what is now Texas.

Roughly 700,000 years later, or 1.3 million years ago, the second but much smaller caldera-forming eruption occurred near the extreme western end of the first. It is called the Henry's Fork or Island Park caldera. It blew out 67 cubic miles of material and was one-tenth as big as the first.

The third came 670,000 years later, or 630,000 years ago, and shot 240 cubic miles of rock and ash into the sky, or four times as large as its predecessor. Its ash spread was similar to the first, but shifted further southeast, blanketing much of Oregon and Washington state and extending down to cover nearly all of Texas. Its caldera was so massive — 30 miles wide and 45

miles long, covering the center of the park — it obliterated much of the first caldera

Smith says the amount of material spewed out by these three eruptions would fill the Grand Canyon in Arizona twice over.

(For further comparison, the Mount St. Helens eruption of May 18, 1980, blew out about one-fourth of a cubic mile of material. Its ash fall spread from southwestern Washington eastward across Idaho, into Montana and Wyoming with even a dusting of ash in Denver. Mount St. Helens significantly enlarged its crater but did not collapse into a caldera.)

Let's look at this mass excavation of real estate another way. Prior to those three huge eruptions, there was a mountain range through what is now the park, extending between Mt. Washburn and the Gallatin Range on the north to Mt. Sheridan near Jackson Hole and Teton National Park on the south. That mountain range was leveled. Obliterated. Its peaks looked down on what is now Yellowstone Lake. The currently bulging Sour Creek Dome, pressurized from below, rises again near where these mountains once rose and then collapsed.

This whole area is within the eastern part of the collapsed Yellowstone landscape.

Remember the moving North American plate? It bears a trail of calderas, like Hansel and Gretel's bread crumbs, created by the hot spot.

These three Yellowstone calderas form the northeastern-most manifestations of the hot spot's track that starts on the Nevada-Oregon border with eruptions 16.5 to 15 million years ago, then progresses up the Snake River plain of Idaho to Yellowstone in northwestern Wyoming. Earth scientists have found 142 calderas clustered in seven volcanic "centers" along this path.

One is tempted to say the hot spot is moving northeast because chronologically that's how the eruptions seem to progress — oldest to youngest, southwest to northeast. But remember the plate, part of the earth's upper crust, moves southwest. The hot spot is virtually stationary. The hot spot's track progresses northeast. Think of holding a piece of paper flat and low over a candle flame. Move the paper one direction and watch the scorched line move across the paper in the opposite direction. The direction analogy breaks down in trying to explain why an eruption happens here and not there: the plate's substance is not as consistent as a sheet of paper. Smith points out that normal basin and range stretching of the plate — the same phenomenon that built much of the mountainous West — also is partly to blame for this apparent movement of the hot spot.

The Yellowstone caldera huffs and puffs, as some scientists call it, being non-technically descriptive.

Two old resurgent lava domes have been building in the park for a long time. They are the Mallard Lake dome near Old Faithful and the Sour Creek dome near the outlet of Yellowstone Lake, at its north end. Sour Creek began after the huge eruption of 630,000 years ago and has grown about 1,200 feet above its neighboring terrain. Mallard is younger, starting to rise from its surrounding plateau about 150,000 years ago. Motorists pass over the southern shoulder of Mallard dome when driving between Old Faithful and West Thumb on Yellowstone Lake.

Repeated inflation and deflation of Yellowstone's surface drew Kenneth L. Pierce, of the USGS and Northern Rocky Mountain Science Center at Montana State University, and his research colleagues to measure such movements by studying surface features.

Since the last glaciers, or about 14,500 years ago, the central Yellowstone caldera's breathing — inflation and deflation — has nearly balanced out with subsidence slightly exceeding uplift, as they reported in their 2002 USGS paper, *Post-Glacial Inflation-Deflation Cycles, Tilting, and Faulting in the Yellowstone Caldera Based on Yellowstone Lake Shorelines*.

Of possible causes for these oscillations of the crust — intrusion of new magma or tectonic stretching of the surface — Pierce favors a third mechanism of hydrothermal origin: hot water sealed from escape, then inflation from increased pressure, followed by cracking of the seal, release of pressure, and deflation before repeat of the cycle. His team concluded: "Although the post-glacial deformation record does not indicate voluminous magma accumulation or other large-scale eruption precursors, strong local deformation associated with hydrothermal centers does suggest the possibility of future hydrothermal explosions and associated hazards."

Rather surprisingly, the magma body that heats Yellowstone's thermal system may be closest to the surface not under the resurgent domes, but 12 miles northeast of the caldera. It is under the Hot Springs Basin Group, by area the largest hydrothermal grouping in the park.

In a manuscript prepared for publication in the Journal of Volcanology and Geothermal Research, Katrina R. DeNosaquo, teamed with Smith and Anthony R. Lowry, of the Dept. of Geology at Utah State University, to report finding a uniform 6-mile depth for Yellowstone's magma body under the whole caldera. But under Hot Springs Basin it was just over 4 miles down. DeNosaquo is a former Smith student now with ConocoPhillips in Houston.

Thus "the crust northeast of the mapped caldera may be more susceptible to volcanism than the rest of the caldera" if continued volcanic activity in the park requires new melting, the DeNosaquo team wrote. She cautioned later, in a letter, that her research did not make any attempt to address eruption forecasting.

Since the NeNosaquo finding, Yellowstone National Park registered a notably large swarm of earthquakes — 500 quakes in 10 days — starting Dec. 26, 2008, and located under the floor of Yellowstone Lake. It is an area of historic earthquake activity and near hydrothermal areas under the north end of the lake — thus not far from the shallow magma body noted by DeNosaquo.

Because of the teeming thermal activity beneath Yellowstone's surface, and enabled by refined technology, the Yellowstone Volcano Observatory was established in 2001 to study and monitor the park's volcanism. Smith directs the organization, which is a collaboration between the University of Utah, the USGS, and Yellowstone National Park.

Accelerated uplifts in the caldera were recorded between 2004 and 2006, as reported in the Nov. 9, 2007, issue of Science magazine. Wu-Lung Chang, Smith and their colleagues found rises up to 7 centimeters (2.76 inches) per year, which is more than three times faster than earlier observed one-year periods.

Surface elevation changes to this degree of accuracy are possible with two satellite-based monitoring systems, Interferometric Synthetic Aperture Radar (InSAR) and the Global Position System (GPS). InSAR can provide detailed information on a wide area over a long period of time. It aims radar energy into the ground and then measures the signal's return time. Data is from the European Space Agency's ERS-2 satellite. It is expensive and satellite time can be difficult to schedule. GPS data requires an instrument on the ground to receive information from satellites. It is a more precise version of personal GPS units, such as the one in your pocket or mounted in your car. InSAR data are collected every year or so. The dozen GPS stations scattered around Yellowstone can provide day-to-day information about ground uplift or subsidence.

By comparison, only a fluke allowed scientists to accurately measure ground subsidence in the 1959 Hebgen quake. They had a before-and-after comparison at their disposal because highway survey benchmarks just happened to closely parallel the Hebgen fault scarp and could be integrated with lakeshore changes and other indicators.

A new uplift on the northern rim of the Yellowstone caldera was recorded during the period 1997 to early 2004 when increased thermal activity and heat were noted at Norris Geyser Basin. Within a two-week period, however, the northern rim of the caldera started deflating, or subsiding, and inflation resumed in the main caldera domes to the south, perhaps because of redistribution of hydrothermal fluids. Further, earthquake activity in the park during this period was concentrated in this Norris area, while other parts of the caldera had unusually low rates of seismic events. With fluids migrating from the Norris region into the caldera, earthquakes can be induced between the inflating and deflating areas, Smith and colleagues wrote.

Their interpretation of the cause: recharging of the Yellowstone magma body, meaning rising magma, more magma volume in the plume, more heat, more uplift, compensating deflation elsewhere, and change in seismic patterns, which all equate to more interest and attention by professionals and lay persons alike.

Labeling the source as the Yellowstone hot spot is not only descriptive. It is also emotionally engaging, triggering our "hot buttons," so to speak.

Not everyone believes it.

Warren Hamilton, still an active researcher 50 years after his intense debate with Irving Witkind over Hebgen quake interpretation, does not mince words. He told me in a letter that Smith, as a leading proponent for the Yellowstone plume, "has spent much of his career seeking evidence for this mythical beast, and has yet to find any. It's merely a philosophical concept, for which the only support is the rough northeast progression of magmatic ages (along the Snake River plain), and the speculation that this might be a result of moving a plate over a burner …

"There is, of course, a shallow hot region, but there is no deep plume under Yellowstone," Hamilton contends. "A propagating rift fits the data much better," by which he means the type of earth movement observed as sea floors spread.

In reply, Smith tersely commented, "Hamilton can say whatever he wants to."

In his paper, *Driving Mechanism and 3-D Circulation of Plate Tectonics,* published in 2007 by The Geological Society of America, Hamilton counts himself as one of "the minority of geoscientists" who believe that tectonic plates migrate as a result of top-down geologic dynamics rather than being pushed by deep-core heating, and that heat convection related to plate movement "is a product, not a cause, of plate motions."

"The conventional assumption that plate-tectonic circulation involves the entire mantle and is driven by bottom heating has been repeated and embellished in hundreds of textbooks at all levels and in thousands of scholarly papers, and it has been widely taught as dogma for 30 years," Hamilton wrote.

"Contrarians face great inertia in ingrained biases when arguing that none of the conjectural variants of this conventional wisdom is soundly based."

Hamilton's work in global tectonics and evolution of the earth's crust has earned him two of the highest honors for a geologist, membership in the National Academy of Sciences and the Penrose Medal of the Geological Society of America.

Hamilton refers to the hot spot as "the stovepipe idea" of bringing heat up from deep in the earth. He does not buy it for Yellowstone, or anywhere. "There is not a single place in the world where it has held up. The notion came up first for Hawaii and it was thoroughly disproved there."

His propositions affect the Hebgen and Yellowstone stories and go far beyond, so let us turn back to current research in this region.

"Although the geodetic observations and models do not imply an impending volcanic eruption or hydrothermal explosion," Smith's team concluded, "they are important evidence of on-going processes of a large caldera that was produced by a super volcano eruption."

In other words, it has happened before, and the caldera's huffing and puffing are the kind of signs that MIGHT precede some sort of reactivation. The eruption 640,000 years ago was followed by 30 smaller events, predominantly the explosive rhyolite type. Some were gigantic, such as those creating the Madison and Pitchstone plateaus in the park. The most recent was 70,000 years ago. These numerous eruptions have filled in much of the caldera pits, which now are reforested and lie nearly undetected by the untrained eye.

And what of the underground research?

Fifty years ago, only a handful of seismographs existed in southwestern Montana. Today, we have more complete information. An ongoing study utilizing 86 seismic stations, spread over an area 360 by 300 miles with Yellowstone at its center, was started in 1999. Gregory P. Waite, Smith and Richard A. Allen published their results in the April 2006 edition of the Journal of Geophysical Research.

Their digital image of the underground hot spot shows a plume of molten and semi-solid magmatic material. Its shape suggests a tornado funnel cloud, Fig. 55. Its axis is tilted downward about 60 degrees toward the northwest, nearly as far as Dillon, Montana. Its configuration — a stem-like base rising into a bulbous top — is quite different from images of hot spots in other parts of the world. According to Smith, this hot magmatic plume rises so near to the caldera surface that it has fueled Yellowstone's volcanic history for millions of years, and some of its earthquake history as well.

When a quake shudders the earth, seismic signals from across the 108,000-square-mile array of stations measure and reveal differences in travel times for the shock wave. Sound transmits through materials at different speeds, depending upon the material's properties, that is, slower through gas, liquid, or molten or cracked rock than through solid rock. Temperature also influences travel speed: hot = slower, cool = faster. Computers synthesize these returning signals into a digital, three-dimensional image approximating the actual shape of the magma/anomaly.

Thus earthquakes, through the shock waves they produce, make possible this visualization process, called teleseismic tomography. (When a physician needs a really good noninvasive look at your kidney, a CT scan, short for "computed tomography," might be ordered.) "Seeing" certain changes in the magma body could help predict future volcanic activity, although the technology awaits an actual volcanic event upon which to test any forecasting theory. Conversely, if redistribution of heat from the magma body causes the caldera floor's huffing and puffing, that is, the rise and fall of ground levels within the caldera, the heat is also causing faults and earthquakes. There is interdependence between natural phenomena and the scientific technologies to analyze them.

Still another aspect of Earth's creative dance exists between earthquakes and hydrothermal systems. Just as minerals build up where geysers spray and pool on the surface, subterranean cracks and crevices through which hot water rises can get clogged. As Smith describes it, they suffer from "natural arteriosclerosis" and "need earthquakes to stay alive" — to be shaken open from time to time.

Recent research indicates the Yellowstone plume is cooler than expected — only 130-390 degrees Fahrenheit hotter than its surrounding material, compared with a 570-degree differential for the Hawaiian volcanic system.

"This plume temperature is kind of wimpy with respect to something like Hawaii," says Derek L. Schutt of the Department of Geosciences at Colorado State University. He and Ken Dueker of the University of Wyoming Department of Geology and Geophysics reported their research in the August 2008 issue of the journal *Geology*.

Schutt told me in an interview since publication that tomographic representations of the plume go down to a depth of about 300 miles. "We're not sure whether the plume stops there or we can't see it because we lack the data," says Schutt. "It looks a lot like a mantle plume. We can't think of a near-surface process that could otherwise create such a pipe of low seismic velocities. Those findings along with my temperature work seem to confirm the idea of a plume. But it's hard to understand how something can be a plume and also be so weak."

Schutt and Dueker suggest that the "wimpy" temperature may result from the plume's tail being sheared off from its deep source by the southwesterly progression of the North American plate. As the plume rises up to a depth of about 60 miles, Schutt says, it appears to be pulled southwest in the direction of the North American plate's movement, leaving its old, deep source behind.

Christiansen is one of the geologists who disagrees with the theory of a plume and the depth of its source.

Rather than a deep-core source of upwelling magma, Christiansen and others propose that heat convection within even a very shallow upper mantle is sufficient cause of the Yellowstone hotspot. Further, he cites seismic evidence showing the absence of any deep-mantle plume.

Christiansen sees the Yellowstone hotspot and its three super-volcanoes over the past 2 million years — as well as the track of calderas pointing southwestward along the Snake River Plain — as products of extension and thinning of the earth's crust. Rise of the upper mantle toward the crust and partial melting increases heat flow, decreases rigidity of the crust, or lithosphere, and promotes extension and thinning. The process tends to be cyclical.

The flood basalts covering much of eastern Washington and Oregon are akin to the later propagation of the Yellowstone hotspot, Christiansen believes.

Smith's new research and a summary of his findings about the Yellowstone plume are laid out in a paper planned for publication in the Journal of Volcanology and Geothermal Research later in 2009. He's the lead author with colleagues from Harvard, Michigan, Norway and Switzerland.

The team supports a depth down to about 396 miles for the plume and a possible but "problematic" hot spot kinship with the Columbia Plateau basalt field of eastern Oregon and Washington, but for reasons different from Christiansen's.

They picture these elements, in descending order: the central Yellowstone National Park plateau, that is, the floor of the caldera; about 6 miles below the surface a horizontal magma body 8-15 percent melted, about 6 miles thick and 24 by 36 miles in dimension, but expanding; the top of a plume about 36 miles below the magma body; the plume ending, or at least disappearing from tomographic view, about 396 miles down.

Smith acknowledges controversial points in the theory.

The paper, when still in pre-publication review, said: "The Yellowstone may be a beheaded remnant of a stronger plume that could have originated at the core-mantle boundary. Such a feature would have originated in the lower mantle but was cut off by the high angle of tilt, leaving melt from a more limited thermal source in the transition zone. The remaining material would have a low buoyancy flux (or upwelling) characteristic of a weaker plume," a description similar to Schutt and Dueker's description of the plume's "wimpy" nature.

The question of *how* the plume heats the magma body — separated by 36 miles — is one of the unresolved Yellowstone problems acknowledged by Smith. Also poorly understood is the relationship between faulting and the volcanic system.

There seems to be little disagreement about a shallow magma body heating Yellowstone. The differences dwell in

119

calling its source a plume or a rift or self-propagating, and how far down these processes descend. Deep subjects, these.

Nearly all the earth scientists interviewed about the Hebgen-Yellowstone region regarded differences — sometimes strongly stated — as just part of the territory, something to be expected in open scientific inquiry. Their disagreement does not preclude their cooperation.

For example, take the 2007 open-file report *Preliminary Assessment of Volcanic and Hydrothermal Hazards in Yellowstone National Park and Vicinity.* Christiansen is lead author and Smith is among the co-authors. It is another example in geology of highly regarded scientists reaching different conclusions from the data before them.

Despite the debates about volcanism — interest that is, in part, fueled by its mystery — earthquakes are by far the most common recurring hazards of the Hebgen-Yellowstone region. On that, Christiansen, Smith and others agree. For that reason, it is regrettable that a companion report, a detailed assessment of future earthquake hazards, has yet to be released.

However, a USGS map, Fig. 50, shows a probability of 0.52, or about even, for an earthquake greater than a magnitude of 5 within the next 10 years in the Hebgen Lake area. The same hazards listing, accessed on-line Jan. 28, 2009, projected the probability of a 7.0 quake within 10 years in the same area as nil, 0.00. The map shows a striking similarity to the plotting of the heaviest seismic activity of the past, a trend heading northwest from the Yellowstone caldera, shown in Fig. 49.

The next most likely hazards to occur are hydrothermal, as Pierce's proposal has reported. These would be the type of phenomenon eloquently reported in 1888 by Joaquin Miller following an explosion of the park's Excelsior Geyser: "At each eruption, immediately preceding, was an upheaval of some 50 feet high, followed by one great explosion in which the water was thrown 250 to 300 feet and frequently hurling stones one foot in diameter 500 feet from the crater."

A hydrothermal explosion, small but large enough to pose a risk to people, could be expected once in 10 years. An explosion large enough to form a crater 100 meters wide would have a frequency of once in 200 years.

Probability of future volcanic activity is much lower. For a basaltic flow there is an average recurrence estimated at 16,000 years. For a large rhyolitic lava eruption within the caldera the projection is once every 20,000 years. The probability of an eruption large enough to form another caldera is so small it is not readily quantifiable, but something less than a million years.

Christiansen's team concluded: "Continued monitoring by YVO (Yellowstone Volcano Observatory) is likely to enable recognition of premonitory indications before any volcanic eruption … Certain conditions, such as major earthquakes or seasonal or long-term lowering of local water tables, tend to favor the occurrence of hydrothermal explosions. The YVO monitoring system should at least provide rapid information about any such event once it occurs. Toxic gas releases, especially of CO_2 or H_2S, would probably be recognized only after they occur, mainly by indirect evidence such as dead or distressed plants or animals."

The gases, odorless carbon dioxide and stinky hydrogen sulfide, are the most common toxic vapors emitted from the thermal areas. They caused the death in 1939 of one construction worker and unconsciousness for another, both working in a deep pit at Tower Junction. These two gases, probably trapped near the ground by a cold weather inversion along the Gibbon

River near Norris Geyser Basin, also were believed to have killed five bison in 2004.

Although the probability of future volcanism is slim, the consequences of even a small eruption makes planning and preparation important.

Geoscientists are a courageous lot. They reach for certainty about phenomena. that are nearly imperceptible and whose recurrence usually is much less frequent than once in a lifetime. The passage of time can lull persons to sleep and this brings us back to the question of risk.

Do people behave according to carefully computed tables of probability? Do vacationers pick campgrounds or campsites that way? Or does their passing by a campground such as Rock Creek take any of these factors into account?

Geophyicist Smith was featured speaker at the November 2007 Western Regional Colloquium of the USGS in Menlo Park, CA. His topic was "Geodynamics and Seismic/Geodetic Imaging of the Yellowstone Hot Spot," but he also spoke of his early career.

It was while working alone in the park's back-country that Smith became fascinated with the Yellowstone hot spot. As a risk-taker, he's eased off from his former passion for wilderness skiing, but Smith plainly enjoys talking about his pursuit and analysis of risk, in his work as well as his recreational activities.

When discussing the real risk of future super volcanoes, Smith quickly points out that he owns a family retreat near Moose, Wyoming, near the Tetons and not far from Yellowstone, well within the potential danger zone of another large eruption. The only disruptions to the peace he has found there, he says, were the occasional motorcades of black Secret Service SUVs and the overhead "whop, whop, whop" of security helicopters

when Vice President Cheney visited his retreat at nearby Jackson Hole.

In *Windows into the Earth,* Smith says that much of the North American Plate has pushed past the hot spot. Earth's crust has been stretched and thinned by the same tectonic forces that shaped the western United States into ranges and basins. Next in line, however, northeast of the Yellowstone calderas, are rocks that are thicker, colder, and stronger, he says, making an eruption more difficult. He allows that the rise of molten rock may completely end, and only time will tell — time, as in millions of years.

Christiansen, writing for the USGS, describes several possible scenarios, none imminent, and closes his detailed paper with this cautious proposition: "It is reasonable to postulate voluminous ash-flow eruption and caldera formation from a new ring-fracture zone in the vicinity of the Firehole River drainage basin. How real and how distant such prospects might be cannot now be quantitatively assessed."

The Firehole drainage is the location of Old Faithful. It is the most popular region for tourists, who are not being kept away by predictions like Smith's and Christiansen's.

I've talked to many people who live or work in this Yellowstone region without encountering a single one who is holding his or her breath, or changing their lifestyle or their addresses because of earthquakes or the hot spot.

The same goes for other potential hazards, such as the crippled but apparently sturdy Hebgen Dam nearly everyone feared would break apart the night of the quake.

Nancy and Charles Sperry formerly operated Campfire Lodge Resort, a cabin-campsite-restaurant business — with wonderful breakfasts — established in 1928 along the Madison River about a mile below the dam. When they looked it over before buying, 24 years after the Hebgen quake, Chuck joked, "Only an idiot would own a place below that dam." They bought it anyway and stayed for 26 years.

Few guests talked of it, Nancy says. "New guests are a bit nervous about the dam and talk about it after going to the Visitors Center, but not the old guests. Some came annually for 40 years."

Until 2005, the Sperrys lived there the year around and felt only three quakes. One damaged a 200-foot well that had to be re-drilled. Another forced repair of some bent underground pipes. The other merely shook things up without damage.

"I lived there 26 years and never lost a night's sleep over it," Chuck says of the resort's location. "If you got to go, you might as well go all at once."

In 1983 the Sperrys also became concessionaires operating the Forest Service's Cabin Creek Campground just across the highway from Campfire, Fig. 26. It had then, and still has, tent sites less than a hundred feet from the west end of the Hebgen fault scarp, where the ground fell about 12 feet. The Sperrys say the campground is laid out just as it was in 1959, except for a shower house that was situated only 10 feet away when the fault scarp dropped. The building survived the quake without great damage, but was removed by the Forest Service in the 1980s.

Jim and Wendy Slatery (Fig. 46), who bought Campfire from the Sperrys in the spring of 2008, had never heard of the Hebgen quake before they came one summer to fish. When Wendy stepped into one of the cabins, she had a *déjà vu* experience. "I've been here before," she said. That was the clincher.

When I spoke with them in September 2008, their campground and cabins were temporarily closed by Forest

Service edict as a safety precaution. A malfunction of outlet controls in Hebgen Dam's penstock quadrupled the Madison River's normal out-flow from the lake. For several days, until the outlet was repaired, engineers showed extreme caution, in part because of the dam's history. Detection of a small earthquake reported the morning of the malfunction added to the fears.

That first season treated the Slaterys harshly. Highway construction delayed their spring opening and the new dam scare prematurely ended their season and the favored autumn fishing.

Their canyon home, though, is heaven to them, he from New Jersey and she from California. "See that cross up on the rock cliff?" Wendy asks, pointing. "They say it formed in the rocks the night of the quake, fifty years ago. Folks woke to discover the cracks in the rocks the next morning." She and Jim take it as a good sign.

Science and faith sometimes mix when we ask people to reflect on life events that remain unexplained.

"Location of a fault was never a consideration in where we lived in the Bay Area," says geologist Schwartz. "We simply moved into the house that we liked at the time. But I'd say that is not true for everybody.

"My wife is a realtor. I get questions all the time about 'If I don't want to be close to a fault, where in the Bay Area should I move?' Around here you can move away from a fault but you can't move very far from shaking ground and that's what really does the damage.

"Most people just don't worry about this on a daily basis. There are so many other pressures in your daily life. Unless there was an earthquake the night before that you felt, I think it is a very abstract concept and people by and large just don't think about it. For most people," says Schwartz, "it's out of sight, out of mind."

All the survivors interviewed for this story have revisited the Madison Canyon, some with uneasy feelings but all feeling good about returning to a place where they had fun, but also might have died. John Owen fishes in the canyon with friends almost every summer. Bonnie Schreiber goes back fairly often but some loud rumbling sounds make her think of 50 years ago. Irene Bennett Dunn stayed away for years before a friend urged her to return. The healing was so helpful she was able to write her book about the family tragedy.

Time heals — people and broken land forms.

Weathering and erosion soften or obliterate much of the slumping soil of fault scarps, sand boils and such.

People forget, and they also create. Each person carries stories of past events, skipping over some details, emphasizing others — a reality that in no way implies forgetfulness or even dishonesty. These stories become ballast for our memories and emotional needs, reconciling us with our experiences and their consequences.

Geologist Hamilton and his wife revisited the area in 1995, 36 years after the quake and slide, and found that the then-new occupants of Blarneystone Ranch bulldozed over a section of the Red Canyon fault scarp without realizing what it was, being somehow unaware of its history.

Nearby, numerous families have built homes along the Red Canyon scarp, apparently oblivious to its history or confident, convinced a repeat will not happen in their lifetime or exceed their insurance coverage.

Forgetting is not part of the agenda for volcanoes and earthquakes. These natural forces do what they do without planning or consideration of consequences or reflection upon what has happened.

Exploring causes for catastrophic events, Amos Nur authored, with Dawn Burgess, the book *Apocalypse: Earthquakes, Archaeology, and the Wrath of God,* published in 2008. They contend some of the destruction of buildings, cities, and even civilizations in ancient history may have resulted from earthquakes rather than from attacks by victorious armies or bands of marauders. Earthquakes happen so rarely, perhaps they are easier to forget than human drama. Nur is the Wayne Loel Professor of Earth Sciences and professor of geophysics at Stanford University.

"Perhaps my greatest goal in writing this book is simply to convince archaeologists who work on sites in the earthquake belts of the world that, when uncovering physical destruction — collapsed walls and buildings, colonnades, crushed skeletons, offset keystones — earthquakes should be considered as one of the foremost possible causes of the devastation," Nur writes.

But whatever the cause may be, we humans, in hindsight, often attribute meaning to nature's forces and contemplate natural phenomena happening in relation to our own choices and actions — for our personal internal balance as survivors and witnesses, as well as for the silent victims. In other words, we hold on to stories to explain the experience the best way we are able.

The Hebgen Lake earthquake and slide of 1959 gave, in our lifetime, a view of both nature's earth-building processes and intimate human experience and interpretation of the events.

We wisely expend much energy wondering when and if and under what circumstances such disaster might happen again. Perhaps as important, however, will be our responses to whatever occurs when the time comes.

Along with grief for the human tragedy comes this awesome opportunity to witness Earth's re-creation as it happens.

Appendix

Earthquake Victims

The 19 persons believed to be buried under the slide are:

- Sidney D. and wife Margaret Ballard, and their son Christopher, of Nelson, B.C.
- Bernie L. and wife Inez Boynton, of Billings, MT.
- Dr. Merle and wife Edna Edgerton, of Coalinga, CA.
- Roger and wife Elizabeth Provost and sons Richard, 16, and David, 1, of Soledad, CA.
- Marilyn Stowe, of Sandy, UT.
- Robert J. and his wife Edith Coy Williams, and children Steven, 11, Michael, 7, and Christy, 3, of Idaho Falls, ID.
- Harmon and his wife Edna Woods, of Coalinga, CA.

Other victims of the quake and slide were:

- Purley Bennett and children Carole, 17, Tom, 10, and Susan, 5, of Coeur d'Alene, ID. Their bodies were found in the river bed downstream from the slide.
- Thomas Mark Stowe, of Sandy, UT, whose body also was found below the slide.
- Mr. and Mrs. E. H. Stryker, of San Mateo, CA, were killed by a massive falling boulder at Cliff Lake, about six miles west of the slide.
- Myrtle Painter, of Ogden, UT, and Margaret Holmes, of Billings, MT, were injured in the campground upstream from the slide and died later at a Bozeman, MT, hospital.

Glossary

Aftershocks — Subsequent shaking of the ground resulting from or somehow relating to the initial earthquake, usually growing weaker gradually.

Alluvium — Material such as silt, clay, sand or gravel carried into place by streams or other running water.

Armageddon — A metaphor for any great conflict or battle, but usually used in a religious sense imaging a future, final battle between good and evil, and an end to the world as we know it.

Basalt — Often gray or black, fine-grained volcanic rock extruded from the earth. Large masses cool slowly and can form impressive vertical columns, polygonal in cross-section, sometimes exposed by highway construction or stream erosion.

Buttress — A wall-like barrier or support.

Colluvium — A loose deposit of earthen material deposited by gravity at the base of a slope or cliff. Mudslides and landslides produce colluvium. Deposits may take shape rapidly or result from slow, gradual slumping of material. Mudslides might not occur without some intrusion of water to provide lubrication.

Cormorants — Usually dark sea or inland birds of medium to large size. These fish eaters often perch on rock cliffs or trees and dive to feed, propelling themselves under water with their webbed feet. At Earthquake Lake, they often perch on the top branches of dead trees killed by the rising lake.

Dolomite — A sedimentary, carbonate rock composed of calcium magnesium carbonate. Limestone partially replaced by dolomite is called dolomitic limestone. Dolomite is used for ornamental stone and concrete aggregate. It is often the reservoir rock for petroleum. Sometimes it is crushed and used as a flux to remove impurities from metals in smelting, or by nurseries as a "sweetener" to reduce acidity in potting soils.

Epicenter — The surface location directly above the hypocenter or underground focus of an earthquake, often miles below.

Fan — Soil and silt dropped by water where it empties into a lake, ocean or slower moving water, usually forming a triangular shape, or delta.

Fault — The fracture of rock that produces earthquakes (although until nearly the mid-20th century, it was thought that earthquakes caused faults). In a normal fault, one rock face drops in relation to its opposing face. It is also an extension, or stretching, of the earth's crust and may fall away from the opposing face. In a strike-slip fault, the fault surface is nearly vertical and the opposing sides of the fracture slide horizontally left or right. A thrust fault develops in a state of compression—versus extension—in which one side of the fracture is pushed up and over the other; these are the compression forces that produce mountain ranges.

Fault Scarp — The scar or deformation on the earth's surface that is a manifestation of the underground fault in bedrock. After a few years of wind and water erosion and new plant growth, scarps may slump and escape detection by the untrained eye.

Glacial Till — Gravel, sand and soil pushed into place by a moving glacier or dropped from the glacier's icy grip during melting.

Gneiss — Pronounced (nais) is a common metamorphic rock, usually exhibiting layers of materials, or foliation. With biotite-rich schist, gneiss was the predominant rock of the Madison Canyon slide. The newest USGS geologic map of the area classifies the material with the region's other earth flow and landslide deposits of angular pebbles, the cobbles and boulders associated with fine-grained matrix of silt and sand.

Lichen — A growth, often clinging to trees or rocks, which represents a symbiotic partnership between a fungus and one or more algae and/or cyanobacteria. When other forage is sparse, lichens provide food for mountain goats, for instance.

Lithosphere — The lithosphere is the solid, outermost layer of the Earth, made up of the crust and the upper mantle. It is a rigid shell and deforms through fracturing, such as faults. Lying under this is the asthenosphere, which is the weaker, pliable, hotter, and deeper part of the upper mantle. The asthenosphere is softened by heat and has plastic characteristics and can flow when under strain.

Magma Chamber — Magma is the mixture of molten and solid rock rising from the earth's mantle that creates a volcanic eruption if and when it finds—or creates—a pathway through the lithosphere to the surface.

Mantle — The mantle makes up approximately 70 percent of the planet, encapsulating the inner and outer core and lying below the relatively very thin crust of the earth, or lithosphere. The mantle consists of a combination of molten and solid material which forms a viscous, slowly flowing mass. Partial melting of the mantle produces the crust as more buoyant components float upward, cool and solidify. Yellowstone National Park is over a magma chamber that is high in the lithosphere, unusually close to the surface, and fuels the park's spectacular thermal phenomena.

Metamorphosis, metamorphosed — In geology, rocks that have changed characteristics because of heat and pressure.

Rocks that become hot enough to melt before hardening again also take on new characteristics, but are igneous.

Moraine — A ridge or mound of soil, gravel, and rocks carried or pushed ahead by an advancing glacier, but left behind as the melting ice retreats. A terminal moraine is the marker of a glacier's furthest advance.

Obsidian — A natural glass found in the Yellowstone region, formed when rhyolites cool too quickly to grow crystals.

Orogeny — Greek for "mountain generating." The Laramide Orogeny is the period of time, 70 to 80 million years ago, during which much of the mountainous west took its shape, rocks under compression thrusting upward to form mountains. Earlier orogenies are the Nevadan and Sevier. Laramide evidence can be found from northern Mexico to Alaska and as far east as the Black Hills in South Dakota. The name comes from the Laramie Mountains of eastern Wyoming.

Paleoseismology — The study of rocks and sediments for traces of ancient earthquakes.

Plate Tectonics — The phenomenon of large sections of the earth's crust, lithosphere, which move in relation to the upper mantle, or asthenosphere, lying below. The North American Plate moves toward the southwest, jamming against the Pacific Plate along the Pacific Coast. Other major plates are the African, Antarctic, Australian, Indian (covering the Indian subcontinent and part of the Indian Ocean), Eurasian, and South American. The driving force for plate movement is debated, some citing heat transfer fired from below. Others say that, as the crust

128

cools and thickens, its greater density allows it to sink deeper into the upper mantle and thus power plate motion.

Plastic Flow — Masses of broken rocks of all sizes appear to have behaved like fluid in the Madison Canyon slide, flowing down the south canyon wall and up the north side.

Richter Scale — The measure of earthquake magnitude developed in 1935 by Charles F. Richter and associate Beno Gutenberg, both of the California Institute of Technology. References in this work use Richter because it is the most commonly used scale. It suffers inaccuracy, however, at the lowest and highest extremes of the scale.

Schist — A weak metamorphic rock which, by definition, contains more than 50 percent platy and elongated minerals. The word comes from the Greek word "to split." The rock's components split off easily as flakes or slabs. Biotite schist, found in the Madison Canyon slide, is often interlayered with the dolomitic marble such as the buttress which gave way in the Hebgen Lake earthquake allowing the huge slide.

Seiche — The lateral movement of a body of water caused by earth movement such as an earthquake. In the case of the Hebgen quake, with a significant subsidence of the earth's surface along the northwest shoreline of Hebgen Lake, water from the upper reaches of the lake poured to the northwest to restore its level. The lake slowly sloshed back and forth, in diminishing waves, for nearly 12 hours.

Strata, plural — In the geologic sense, layers of rock laid down over time, often as sediment settling out of a body of water or stream. Stratum, singular.

Subsidence — In this case, the nearly vertical drop of the land and water of the West Yellowstone basin and nearby mountains. The Hebgen fault block, its northern side nearly paralleling Hebgen Lake's northern shore, subsided 22 feet at its deepest

fall. The Red Canyon fault block, adjacent and north of the Hebgen block, subsided as much as 15 feet. Both blocks tilted to the north.

Triangulation — Location of a map point by measuring angles to it from known points. It was the major method used for large-scale surveys until the 1980s and development of global positioning systems. Trilateration was a similar method used for a spherical surface.

Uniformitarianism — Discussing this idea is a Pandora's Box as part of the longstanding dispute between creationists and evolutionists about origins of the earth and its inhabitants. Its summary phrase is "the present is the key to the past." The theory arose in the late 18th and early 19th centuries to explain Earth's formation as resulting from age-old geologic processes still visible and operating today. It was contrary to views of the earth's form resulting from supposedly isolated catastrophic events, called Catastrophism., or from events proclaimed to be miraculous, as in Creationism. This book views the earth's phenomena — such as the earthquake(s), the major fault block subsidence of the West Yellowstone basin, the Madison Canyon rockslide, and the high heat flow from the Yellowstone Plateau—not as isolated or unique events but as specific, temporal, observed phenomena which are the contemporary manifestations of a long history of scientific evidence describing similar events and processes, allowing modification of interpretations with the accumulation of new information.

Welded Rhyolite Tuff — Ash ejected during a volcanic eruption, if hot enough when it falls to earth, may consolidate or weld together to form welded tuff. Most of the tuff in the Yellowstone region is welded rhyolite and contains pumice-like, glassy fragments. Crustal rocks such as granites are melted from below by molten basalt, forming rhyolite magma, said to be many times thicker in consistency than basalt magma. Because of this heavy viscosity, rhyolite eruptions are explosive in comparison to the slow lava flows of Hawaii, for example. In explosive eruption, the larger particles fall closer to the vent and finer, airborne ash settles down at greater distances from its source.

References

Breining, Greg, *Super Volcano: The Ticking Time Bomb Beneath Yellowstone National Park,* Voyageur Press, 2007.

Carrara, Paul E., and O'Neill, Michael J., *Tree-ring Dated Landslide Movements and Their Relationship to Seismic Events in Southwestern Montana,* Academic Press, 2003.

Chang, Wu-Lung, Smith, Robert B., Wicks, Charles, Farrell, Jamie M., and Purkas, Christine M., *Accelerated Uplift and Magmatic Intrusion of the Yellowstone Caldera, 2004 to 2006,* Science, vol. 318, November 2007.

Christiansen, Robert L., Foulger, G.R., and Evans, John R., *Upper-Mantle Origin of the Yellowstone Hotspot,* Geological Society of America Bulletin, October 2002.

Christiansen, Robert L., Lowenstern, Jacob B., Smith, Robert B., Heasler, Henry, Morgan, Lisa A., Nathenson, Mankuel, Masin, Larry G., Muffler, L. J. Patrick, and Robinson, Joel E., *Preliminary Assessment of Volcanic and Hydrothermal Hazards In Yellowstone National Park and Vicinity,* USGS, Open-File Report 2007-1071.

Christiansen, Robert L., *The Quarternary and Pliocene Yellowstone Plateau Volcanic Field of Wyoming, Idaho, and Montana,* USGS, Professional Paper 729-G, 2001.

Christopherson, Edmund, *The Night the Mountain Fell,* Yellowstone Publications, 1962.

DeNosaquo, Katrina R., Smith, Robert B., and Lowry, Anthony R., *Density and Lithospheric Strength Models of the Yellowstone-Snake River Plain Volcanic System from Gravity and Heat Flow Data,* in press for Journal of Volcanology and Geothermal Research, 2009.

Doser, Diane I., *Source Parameters and Faulting Processes of the 1959 Hebgen Lake, Montana, Earthquake Sequence,* Journal of Geophysical Research, May 1985, p. 4537-4555.

Dunn, Irene Bennett, *Out of the Night,* Plaudit Press, 1998.

Haller, Kathleen M., compiler, with Montana Bureau of Mines and Geology, *Complete Report for Hebgen Fault (Class A) No. 656,* USGS, 1993,

Hamilton, Warren B., *Driving Mechanisms and 3-D Circulation of Plate Tectonics,* Geological Society of America Special Paper 433, p. 1-25, 2007.

Hintzman, Davis E., *Physiographic Features of the Madison River Canyon Earthquake Area,* U. S. Forest Service, date undetermined.

Hooper, Peter R., *The Columbia River Basalts and Yellowstone Hot Spot: A Mantle Plume?,* mantleplumes. org, 2007.

Husen, Stephan, Smith, Robert B., and Waite, Gregory P., *Evidence for Gas and Magmatic Sources Beneath the Yellowstone Volcanic Field from Seismic Tomographic Imaging,* Journal of Volcanology and Geothermal Research, vol. 131, pp. 397-410, 2004.

Link, L. W., *The Great Montana Earthquake,* published at Cardwell, MT, 1961.

Lowenstern, Jacob B., and Hurwitz, Shaul, *Monitoring a Supervolcano in Repose: Heat and Volatile Flux at the Yellowstone Caldera,* Mineralogical Society of America Elements, 2008 4: 35-40.

Marler, George, D., *Inventory of Thermal Features of the Firehole River Geyser Basins and Other Selected Areas of Yellowstone National Park,* USGS, GD 73-018, 1973.

Nur, Amos, and Burgess, Dawn, *Apocalypse: Earthquakes, Archaeology, and the Wrath of God,* Princeton University Press, 2008.

O'Neill, Michael J., and Christiansen, Robert L., *Geologic Map of the Hebgen Lake Quadrangle, Beaverhead, Madison and Gallatin Counties, Montana, Park and Teton Counties, Wyoming, and Clark and Fremont Counties, Idaho,* USGS, 2004.

O'Neill. Michael J., LeRoy, Thomas H., and Carrara, Paul E., *Preliminary Map Showing Quaternary Faults and Landslides in the Cliff Lake 15' Quadrangle, Madison County, Montana, USGS,* 1994.

Pierce, Kenneth L., Cannon, K.P., Meyer, G.A., Trebesch, M.J., and Watts, R.D., *Post-Glacial Inflation-Deflation Cycles, Tilting, and Faulting in the Yellowstone Caldera Based on Yellowstone Lake Shorelines,* Chap. E, USGS Professional Paper 1717, 2007.

Schutt, Derek L., and Dueker, Ken, *Temperature of the Plume Layer Beneath the Yellowstone Hotspot,* Geology, Aug. 2008; v. 36; no. 8; p. 623-626.

Schwartz, David P., Hecker, S., and Stenner, H. D., *Hebgen Lake Revisited: Implications for the Behavior and Paleoseismology of Normal Faults,* USGS.

Schwartz, David P., unpublished paper, Power Point presentation delivered to Basin and Range Summit 2 at Reno, NV, 2004.

Smith, Robert B., and Siegel, Lee J., *Windows Into the Earth,* Oxford University Press, 2000.

Smith, Robert B., Jordan, Michael, Steinberger, Bernhard, Puskas, Christine M., Farrell, Jamie, Waite, Gregory P., Husen, Stephan, Chang, Wu-Lung, and O'Connell, Richard, *Geodynamics of the Yellowstone Hotspot and Mantle Plume: Seismic and GPS Imaging, Kinematics, Mantle Flow,* in press for Journal of Volcanology and Geothermal Research, 2009.

U. S. Geological Survey, Dept. of the Interior, Geological Survey Professional Paper 435, *The Hebgen Lake, Montana, Earthquake of Aug. 17, 1959,* 1964.

Waite, Gregory P., and Smith, Robert B., *Seismotectonics and Stress Field of the Yellowstone Volcanic Plateau from Earthquake First-motions and Other Indicators,* Journal of Geophysical Research, vol. 109, B02301, 2004.

Waite, Gregory P., Smith, Robert B., and Allen, Richard M., *Vp and Vs Structure of the Yellowstone Hot Spot from Teleseismic Tomography: Evidence for an Upper Mantle Plume,* Journal of Geophysical Research, vol. 111, B04303, 2006.

Witkind, Irving J., and others, *The Hebgen Lake, Montana, Earthquake of Aug. 17, 1959,* USGS, Professional Paper 435, 1964.

Witkind, Irving J., Myers, W. Bradley, Hadley, Jarvis B., Hamilton, Warren, and Fraser, George D., *Geologic Features of the Earthquake at Hebgen Lake, Montana, Aug. 17, 1959,* Bulletin of the Seismological Society of America, vol. 52, no. 2, pp. 163-180, April 1962.

Witkind, Irving J., *The Night the Earth Shook: A Guide to the Madison River Canyon Earthquake Area,* U. S. Forest Service, Dept. of Agriculture, 1962.

Yellowstone Volcano Observatory, *Satellite Technologies Detect Uplift in the Yellowstone Caldera,* USGS and University of Utah, 2007

Quick Order Form

Name: _____

Shipping Address: _____

City: _____ State: _____ Zip: _____

Daytime telephone: _____

Email address: _____

Send me _____ copies of *CATACLYSM: When Human Stories Meet Earth's Faults*

@ $17.95 each. Total $ _____

Sales tax: Add your local sales tax rate only if a Washington State resident. $ _____

Shipping in U.S.: $4.00 for first book, $2.00 for each additional copy. $ _____

Total: $ _____

(Enclose check or U.S. money order. Order shipped when payment received.)

Send postal orders to: Skifoot Press, PO Box 9715, Spokane, WA 99209

Order online at: www.skifootpress.com

About the Author

Douglas W. Huigen

The author worked as a journalist with The Associated Press and The Denver Post as well as other newspapers in Montana, Iowa and Washington. He also served as a clergyman in Colorado and Montana, and has degrees in Technical Journalism and Theology. Huigen now lives in Spokane, Washington. This is his first book.